World University Library

The World University Library is an international series
of books, each of which has been specially commissioned.
The authors are leading scientists and scholars from all over
the world who, in an age of increasing specialisation, see the
need for a broad, up-to-date presentation of their subject.
The aim is to provide authoritative introductory books for
university students which will be of interest also to the general
reader. Publication of the series takes place in Britain,
France, Germany, Holland, Italy, Spain, Sweden and
the United States.

J. Andrade e Silva
and G. Lochak

Quanta

Translated from the French
by Patrick Moore

Preface by Louis de Broglie
Nobel prize for Physics, 1929

World University Library

McGraw-Hill Book Company
New York Toronto

In the diagrams red is used throughout for waves and blue for particles

530.12
AN2q
85212
Oct 1923

© J. Andrade e Silva and G. Lochak 1969
Translation © George Weidenfeld and Nicolson Limited 1969
Library of Congress Catalog Card Number 68–13139
Phototypeset by BAS Printers Limited, Wallop, Hampshire, England
Printed by Officine Grafiche Arnoldo Mondadori, Verona, Italy

Contents

Preface

Preface

In this book Joào Andrade e Silva and Georges Lochak, who have worked closely with me for many years, show how the discovery of quanta by Planck in 1900 abruptly changed the course of development of classical physics. At once, the discovery raised the difficult problem of the co-existence of waves and particles in light (Einstein, 1905) and in matter (Louis de Broglie, 1923–24). From 1927 onward most theorists gave quantum physics a purely abstract form of construction. Everyone must admire the accuracy and strictness of this 'quantum mechanics', and everyone must recognise that its predictions have been very exact. Yet it is easy to question the validity of the physical reality lying behind this formalism. Modern theorists refuse to re-establish the idea of the localisation of the particle in its wave, but is not this the only way of giving the notion of a particle a precise meaning? And would not this give quantum physics an added force, comparable with that given to thermodynamics by scientists such as Boltzmann and Gibbs, when they introduced the concept of localised atoms and were led to develop what we now call statistical thermodynamics? It was this which made clear the real meaning of entropy and allowed the prediction of some phenomena which had not been accounted for by any of the earlier theories.

In this clear and easily-understood book the authors have succeeded in describing the origin and development of quantum physics, and have gone on to explain the generally-accepted solution. They give reasons for supposing that this solution may not be the final answer, and they suggest something that may eventually replace it. To write such a book needed the great overall knowledge of the two authors, who had also to study and re-examine all the basic texts written since the beginning of our century by the great theoretical physicists – texts which, incidentally, are all too often ignored by many of our young research workers. It was also necessary to give careful consideration to the ideas of the Copenhagen School and to the present-day concepts which are taught under the general heading of quantum mechanics. Finally, it was essential to have full knowledge of the concepts which I took up once more a few years ago, and which the authors and I are trying to extend and improve.

I consider that the authors have been successful in the difficult task that they have set themselves. To me their text seems excellent. I also admire the very capable way in which they describe the ideas I was working on at the time of the discovery of wave mechanics and the interpretations that I proposed in 1927 in my *Theory of Double Solution*. It is this interpretation to which I have returned during the last fifteen years and which I think I have considerably improved, largely with their help. Recently, this work has resulted in my *Thermodynamique cachée des particules* which, I believe, opens up great new possibilities in quantum physics.

In conclusion, let me express the hope that this book will be widely read with the attention that it deserves and that it will lead certain research workers to make a deeper study of the reinterpretation of wave mechanics along the lines that we are now following. Particular note should be taken of the literature mentioned in the bibliography. I believe that this new orientation of the theory of quantum phenomena will give a clearer picture of the co-existence of waves and particles and I hope that it will lead to a better understanding and to easier predictions of these phenomena. In the long run true ideas will always prove to be fruitful.

LOUIS DE BROGLIE
Nobel Prize for Physics, 1929

1 Two small dark clouds

1 Two small dark clouds

Starting point

The first golden age of science lasted from the time of Thales to that of Archimedes. During this period, great progress was made in both mystical and rational thought. Then, however, the study of the laws of nature became submerged in a scholasticism from which it did not break free for fifteen centuries. When it finally emerged, men such as Kepler, Galileo, Descartes and Newton created the new physics, which may have lacked the dreams and poetry of the Greeks, but was far more rigorous and far easier to apply in practice. Pythagoras' idea of the music of the spheres, with the celestial bodies taking part in a choral dance around the central fire of the universe, was intriguing, but the new physics created a 'music' which, although more complicated, was far more effective.

This new physics provided so much more accurate ideas about space, time and gravitation that tremendous advances became possible. The planet Neptune was discovered by calculation before it was actually identified by the telescope. The wave properties of light, and its electromagnetic nature, were found. The meanings of colour, sound, heat and electricity were explained. The analysis of starlight paved the way for a chemical analysis of the stars themselves. The elements were classified, and Hertzian waves, x-rays and radioactivity were discovered.

Einstein once said that 'the most incomprehensible thing about our universe is that it is comprehensible'. Our naïve confidence that all natural phenomena can be explained scientifically is due to the achievements of classical physics. And it is also classical physics which gives constant hope to those people who spend their whole lives studying the problems to which they can never find a complete solution.

By the end of the nineteenth century, this confidence was so strong, and scientists held such radical views, that the infallibility and eternity of classical physics was not doubted. Its progress had been so brilliant, and its successes so great, that the fundamental laws of the universe seemed to have been discovered. One celebrated theorist said that future work would be simply a matter of 'adding a few decimal places to results already obtained' – a view which gives a good idea of the mental outlook of physicists of that time.

One exceptionally brilliant research worker who foresaw the difficulties of classical physics was William Thomson, who was a child prodigy. He entered the University of Glasgow in 1834, when he was ten years old, and six years later he published his first scientific paper. He remained very active all through his long life, and tackled theoretical problems and their practical applications with equal ease. He was given the title of Lord Kelvin, and became a foremost authority in European scientific circles. It was he who declared that it seemed to him that physics was a constant assembling of facts which were in basic agreement with each other and of which the most important had been discovered. On the horizon he saw only 'two small dark clouds'; the negative results of the Michelson-Morley experiment, and the ultra-violet catastrophe of the Rayleigh-Jeans law.

These technical terms will be meaningless to the non-physicist, who cannot be blamed for missing the point of the story. For the moment, then, it is enough to say that Kelvin's two little clouds became so dark that before they were dispersed, everything that was known about space, time, mass and motion had to be re-appraised. One of the clouds led to the theory of relativity; the other to quanta. Looking back at Kelvin's comment, it is not easy to decide which is the more surprising – his honesty in his belief of the completeness of science, or the insight which enabled him to pinpoint the origin of the trouble even though he did not believe in it.

In its decline, classical physics provides the ultimate lesson that even the greatest of scientific doctrines can eventually reach the end of its concepts and experiments, so that it must be replaced by a new doctrine. The heritage which classical physics has left us is immortal, and shows up in every twist and turn of modern physics. As a complete culture, physics is a whole which could not advance if it discarded all its past. This is why in this book, devoted to quantum theory, it is so necessary to start by going back to the main ideas of classical physics, and to the Cartesian description of the world 'by pictures and motion'.

A world without fantasy

The first and perhaps the most elegant theory in classical physics was the science of mechanics, which deals with the laws of motion. Its basic principles were quite straightforward, and its applications were so far-reaching that mechanics spread far beyond its original boundaries. For a long time it affected the whole progress of human thought, and all the materialistic philosophy of the eighteenth century was an extension of it. Until the beginning of our own century, it was true to say that physics was an attempt to understand the world by mechanical concepts alone.

The story began with Galileo, the father of modern physics, who declared that the book of Nature must be written in mathematical symbols. Of all his discoveries, the greatest was that a body upon which no outside force is acting will continue in its state of motion; if it is at rest, it will remain at rest, but it will maintain any velocity that it originally has. This is the *principle of inertia*, the first of the great principles of physics, of which the general statement was probably given by his contemporary René Descartes.

It is not easy for us to realise the revolutionary character of this idea because it is so familiar, but for Galileo and Descartes it meant contradicting the teaching of Aristotle, who was regarded as the supreme authority. Aristotle had believed that a force is necessary to maintain continuous motion. Quite apart from opposing Aristotle, Galileo's idea seemed to go against everyday experience. After all, a cart will stop moving when there is nobody to pull it, while a rolling stone will eventually come to rest unless some force acts upon it to keep it moving.

The genius of Galileo and Descartes was that they paid careful attention to a few simple facts. The cart will move more easily when its wheels are oiled, and the stone will roll further on a waxed surface than on a rough one. What stops them is friction, which acts upon all bodies. A body under ideal conditions of motion will not be subject to friction, and so there will be no forces acting upon it; it will maintain its state of motion indefinitely. Unlike Aristotle, Galileo believed that *natural* motion must be perpetual.

After Galileo and Descartes came that giant of giants Isaac Newton, who, singlehanded, went a long way toward completing the science of mechanics. He started where they had left off, and his first task was to generalise the law of inertia. He asked himself the following question: If, in the absence of all outside forces, the velocity of a body remains unaltered, what is the connection between force and motion? Nowadays, the answer seems obvious enough: the effect of the force is to modify the velocity, that is, to produce an *acceleration*. After making a few basic investigations, Newton concluded that the acceleration given to a body by any particular force will be independent of the form, dimensions and constitution of the body; it will depend entirely upon the amount of matter that the body contains – in other words, its *mass*. The fundamental law of dynamics is:

$$F = m\gamma$$

where **m** is the mass of the moving body, **F** the force acting on it, and γ the acceleration produced. This law shows quite clearly that the only property of a body which is relevant to the study of its motion is the mass. Accordingly, Newton thought that it would be possible to explain the laws of nature by considering matter as made up of geometrical points, with each point having a definite mass and being able to exert a force on every other point.

To be more precise, it should be added that in mechanics the word 'acceleration' does not have the restricted meaning of 'an increase in velocity', as in everyday language. In mechanical terms, a body is subject to acceleration if the amount of ground covered in unit time is changing (either increasing, so that the body is 'accelerating' in the usual sense of the word, or else decreasing, so that the body is decelerating or slowing down). The body is also said to be undergoing acceleration if its direction of motion is changing, even if its actual velocity along its trajectory is not. In either case, Newton's principle states that a force is necessary to modify the motion, and this is clearly demonstrated in everyday life. For instance, power is needed to overcome the inertia of a vehicle and increase its speed, while a braking force is necessary to slow it down. When the vehicle turns a sharp corner, the road exerts a frictional force on the wheels, counteracting the centrifugal force that tends to resist any change in direction.

At first sight it might seem that Galileo's principle of inertia is nothing more than a particular case of this fundamental law of dynamics. According to Newton's principle, if no force is being exerted on a body, the acceleration will also be nil, which brings us straight back to Galileo's principle. Actually, however, matters are much more complicated than might be thought. To explain them, we must make some general comments about the classical definitions of Space and Time.

Up to now, velocity and acceleration have been discussed as though they were absolute concepts. However, the motion of a body can be defined only with respect to other bodies which serve as comparisons, and so make up what is called a system of reference. The law of inertia and the fundamental law of dynamics have no real meaning unless they are referred to a system of reference which has been properly defined. This may be shown by the following example, which brings out the difficulty.

Suppose that we are in a train travelling at 50 km/h, and that we throw a ball in the direction of motion of the train. Assume that the velocity of the ball, relative to the train, is 10 km/h. If we suppose that all the frictional forces acting on the ball are negligible, Galileo's principle tells us that the ball will retain its initial velocity; in other words, it will move on at a velocity of 10 km/h with respect to the train and 60 km/h with respect to the ground. Let us now accelerate the train to 55 km/h. As we have assumed that the ball is rolling along without friction, then the ball has no force acting on it, and its velocity remains unchanged. But unchanged relative to what? With respect to the train, so that its new velocity with respect to the ground is 65 km/h? Or with respect to the ground, so that its new velocity relative to the train becomes 5 km/h? Or must we bring in some other system of reference?

What has been said up to now does not provide an answer to this fundamental question. So far as we know, Galileo never considered it at all. He based his reasoning entirely with respect to the obvious system of reference – the Earth, which was quite adequate for all the problems that concerned him; The law relating to falling bodies is an obvious example. To Galileo, a body at rest was a body at rest *with respect to the Earth*. For a long time this was also the view held by Newton. It was only after he had made the most celebrated of all his discoveries, that of the law of gravitation, that

Newton turned his attention to the problem of space and time.

Fifty years earlier, the great German astronomer Johannes Kepler had been able to draw up three general laws concerning the movements of the planets; he had used the observations made by Tycho Brahe and had interpreted them brilliantly. The first and best-known of Kepler's Laws is that each planet moves round the Sun in an ellipse, with the Sun lying at one of the foci. These were the laws which Newton set out to explain, and he assumed that the laws of dynamics applicable to bodies moving on the surface of the Earth could also be applied to the motions of celestial bodies. Therefore, he assumed that the accelerations of the planets could be put down, quite simply, to the force produced by the pull of the Sun.

Basing his reasoning upon the law of the motions of falling bodies, together with astronomical observations, Newton realised that the force of attraction must be proportional to the product of the mass of the Sun and the mass of the planet, and that it must vary inversely with the square of the distance between them. This was expressed in the famous law of gravitation:

$$F = \frac{mm'}{r^2}$$

Thus as soon as he knew the position of a planet relative to the Sun, Newton could deduce the force that must be acting upon it, and this also gave the acceleration. Also, he showed that this knowledge alone was sufficient for the complete motion of the planet to be worked out, provided that at a given moment the position had been determined and the velocity measured. If the position of the planet for any particular instant is known, it is therefore possible to calculate the force exerted upon it by the Sun at that instant, and so the planet's acceleration can be found. We can also find out how the velocity will change during the short interval of time that follows, and so we can deduce the velocity at the end of this interval. Knowing the velocity of the planet between these two instants, we can find out the distance it must have travelled, and this gives its new position. This in turn gives a new instant for which the velocity and position of the planet have been calculated. The same process can be continued for a third instant, and so on, and step by step the whole motion of the planet can be worked out.

Making use of integral and differential calculus, which he had previously invented, Newton reduced this infinite series of deductions to a rigorous mathematical method. He explained the movements of the planets round the Sun, and those of the Moon round the Earth. He worked out the basic principles behind Kepler's Laws, and he did what astronomers had been trying to do for two thousand years – he reduced the motions of the planets to what may be called a harmony of numbers.

It was then that Newton retraced his steps, and considered the significance of his calculations. Since dynamics had been created to study the movements of objects on and very near the Earth, it had been tacitly assumed that the motions were always to be considered with respect to the Earth, and that the Earth itself was stationary. But this was no longer the case. Now, it had to be assumed that the Sun was motionless, and that all the planets, including the Earth, were revolving round it. The success of his calculations was by itself enough to show that this hypothesis was legitimate, so that the laws of mechanics were valid in a system of reference with the Sun as its basis. And yet how could the laws hold good with respect to the Sun and to the Earth at the same time?

If we accept the principle of inertia, a body upon which no forces are acting will retain its uniform motion in a straight line. If then this principle holds good in a system of reference based on the

Sun, it ought to be false in a system of reference based on the Earth, simply because the Earth revolves round the Sun, and there cannot be straight-line motion simultaneously in two systems revolving round each other. The problem was to explain this apparent experimental contradiction.

Newton managed to do this by pointing out that the ellipse described by the Earth round the Sun is so large, and the Earth's velocity changes so slowly in the course of a year, that for the short interval of time during which the experiment on the Earth's surface is carried out it is quite justifiable to assume that the motion is uniform, and in a straight line with respect to the Sun. The Earth's rotation round its axis can also be neglected, since its effect will, in general, be too slight to influence the result. Moreover, if Newton's laws of mechanics are valid in one particular system of reference, they will be equally valid with respect to a different system of reference which is in a state of uniform straight-line motion relative to the first. This explains why the principles of mechanics are true in a system based on the Sun and also true, at least approximately, in a system based on the Earth.

Newton then asked himself whether it would be sufficient to define the laws of mechanics with respect to the Sun, and not to the Earth. He came to the conclusion that the answer was 'No'. If the acceleration of the whole Solar System could ever be detected with respect to the so-called fixed stars, the system of reference would have to be changed again if real precision were needed. He then had the far-reaching idea of defining space by starting from the laws of motion themselves, and considered a system of reference which was not a physical reality, but was a hypothetical system in which the law of inertia was valid. He was not merely begging the question: he was giving an assumption of the physical world, and, it must be said, a strange assumption at that.

In this way, Newton retained Galileo's principle, and based his dynamics on the hypothesis that a system of reference exists in which *all* bodies with no forces acting on them must remain in a state of unchanging velocity. This principle led him on to define *absolute space* which, he wrote, 'remains, by reason of its nature and without reference to any exterior object, rigorously motionless and steady'. It is in this space that the laws of mechanics govern the movements of bodies.

This seems to be a strange assumption because absolute space is an abstract concept, a kind of protective covering which allows us to make use of *relative space*, defined with respect to the Sun and to the distant stars. The role of absolute space is simply to provide a theoretical foundation for the principles of mechanics. Newton himself said that 'it is quite possible that there is no such thing as a genuinely motionless body to which movements and positions can be referred'.

We must also ask whether it is possible to define velocity and acceleration without an equally elaborate definition of time. The time given by our clocks depends ultimately on the movement of the Earth on itself and around the Sun, or from some other periodical phenomenon. This *relative time* is at the mercy of experimental accuracy and measurement corrections, so that it is unsuitable for the Newtonian conception of mechanics. This is why Newton was led to introduce the idea of *absolute time* as well as absolute space. Absolute time is 'true and mathematical; it is not related to any exterior objects, and it passes in a way which is in accord with its uniform nature . . . relative time is merely a tangible manifestation of absolute time'. Yet 'it is probable that there is no uniform motion which could be used to measure the passage of time exactly'.

This, then, is the essential concept of the world which has been left to us by the genius of Newton. In this abstract scene of absolute space and time, the physical bodies, consisting of geometrical points each of which has definite mass, move according to the laws of proportionality of force and acceleration. What are the forces governing this motion? Newton provided one in his law of gravitation, which formed the basis of celestial mechanics, and which for accuracy has rarely been equalled. The only task left to scientists of future generations was to perfect the work of the master, and to apply his principles to a wider variety of problems, if necessary, by discovering other laws of force to explain new phenomena. Pierre Simon de Laplace, the great French astronomer, once said that anyone who discovered all the laws of force, and who knew at any given instant the positions and velocities of all the masses in the universe, would have a complete knowledge of all the past, the present and the future.

Newton's physical world is a concept both strangely close to and strangely far from actual experience. It was a dull universe, without fantasy, and remained for a long time in the shadow of Laplacian determinism. Later, we shall see how the theory was superseded, and how, ironically, it was the 'material points' which we call atoms which refused to obey the Newtonian laws. But even if classical mechanics is no longer omnipotent, and although its limitations are only too clear, its value remains intact in its own field. In particular, we must not forget that almost all of modern technology is based on Newton's laws. When a rocket is launched from Cape Kennedy or Baikonour toward some distant planet, its trajectory is calculated from Newton's old equations. If, as sometimes happens, the rocket does not reach its target, we may be sure that the failure is due to technical faults – never to the equations.

Revolution by field theory

It was only in the mid-nineteenth century that a new, revolutionary concept was introduced into the history of physics, and it had a profound effect upon Newtonian mechanics. This was the concept of the *field*, which altered the whole outlook about space. According to the new ideas, space was no longer something simple, empty and inert, containing bodies which simply happened to be in a state of movement; it became something with physical properties of its own. These properties could be modified by the presence of material bodies and, conversely, the behaviour of the bodies could be modified by the sort of space in which they were contained. These physical fields, which are just as real as matter itself, have become more and more important. They have invaded optics, following Maxwell; gravitation, with Einstein; and the theory of the atom, with de Broglie. But they were originally born from studies of electricity and magnetism, thanks to the work of Michael Faraday.

Electricity and magnetism are relatively new sciences. Thales of Miletus studied them to some extent, but after his death very little progress was made for two thousand years. It was known that if certain materials, such as amber and glass, are rubbed violently they become able to attract light objects, but this was no real advance upon the knowledge of Thales so long before. It was not until the work of Gilbert, friend of Galileo and doctor to Queen Elizabeth I, that any significant advances were made. Gilbert observed that the curious attracting properties of amber and glass are shared by many other substances, and he developed an ingenious instrument with which he was able to detect the presence of electrical charges.

The existence of magnetic minerals was also known in ancient times, and there is little doubt that the first practical application of magnetism was the invention of the compass, though the actual date of the discovery is uncertain. Yet the phenomenon in itself did not attract the attention of scientists, and again it was Gilbert who made the first notable advances. One of his discoveries was that magnetic poles of the same sign repel each other, while unlike poles attract.

The systematic study of electrical phenomena may be said to have started in the eighteenth century, after which there were rapid developments. By 1750, enough was known about electricity for Benjamin Franklin to be able to interpret lightning as a vast electric spark. Franklin's experiments greatly impressed his contemporaries, and when welcoming the statesman of the young American Republic into the Academy of Sciences in Paris, the mathematician d'Alembert was not afraid to thank him for having 'taken the lightning away from the sky and the sceptre of the tyrant'.

All the research carried out during this period into *static* electricity, or motionless electrical charges, culminated with the experiments of the French engineer Charles Coulomb who, in 1785, found a way of measuring the force acting between two electrical charges **e** and **e**′. Coulomb's measures were extremely accurate, and he was able to show that if **r** is the distance separating the two charges, the force obeys the equation:

$$F = \frac{ee'}{r^2}$$

There is a very clear analogy between this equation and Newton's law of gravitation, and it might have been thought that the science of electricity had been completed by Coulomb's law. Yet some years later, the Italian scientist Alessandro Volta, then a professor at the University of Pavia, introduced new ideas which led electrical science off into a fascinating adventure.

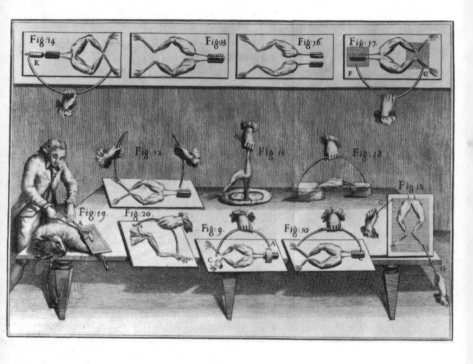

Following upon the researches of his countryman Galvani into what may be called 'animal electricity', Volta put forward the idea of a new physical concept, the *electric current*, that is, electrical charges in motion. His first source of current was obtained by using alternate disks of copper and zinc, separated by rags impregnated with acidified water. The next step was to improve the weak performances of these batteries by building generators of large size. In 1810, the Royal Society in London installed a battery of 2,000 elements. With it, the great chemist Humphry Davy was able to melt all the known metals, and to volatilise diamond.

Volta's work caused intense interest all over Europe, not only among scientists (before his death, he had had honours heaped upon him) but also among the general public, largely because it was thought that electric currents must have miraculous powers. It was even claimed, in all seriousness, that the healing properties of electricity were great enough to cure the mute and the blind. And yet the results of Volta's discovery were miraculous enough in their way: they led to the birth of a new branch of physics – electro-magnetism – which has caused a revolution in both industry and in science.

The Danish scientist Christian Oersted showed the way. After years of unsuccessful attempts, he finally managed to deflect a magnet by passing an electric current close to it, thus showing that there is a close link between electricity and magnetism. This was a great step forward, because up to that time the two phenomena had been thought to be quite unrelated.

Only a few months later, André-Marie Ampère, a professor of astronomy at the Sorbonne, went much further. After consideration of Oersted's work, he had the idea that if an electric current can attract a magnet, showing that the current itself has magnetic properties, then it should be possible to account for all the magnetic phenomena by the means of the properties of electric currents. If so, was it possible that a magnet was simply a piece of material containing a host of microscopic electric currents? To give support to this hypothesis, he had to show that two electric currents can

2 Faraday's disc dynamo. In 1831 Faraday produced the first dynamo by converting magnetism into electricity through electromagnetic induction. He obtained a continuous electric current by turning a copper disc between the poles of a powerful electromagnet. The periphery of the disc was connected to its own axis through a galvanometer.

attract or repel each other, in the same way as magnets do. Ampère carried out the experiment, proved his point, and deduced a general law concerning the mutual effects of electric currents. His *Mathematical Theory of Electrodynamical Phenomena Entirely Deduced from Experimentation* is a model of precision and clarity which has been envied by many later generations of theorists.

Next came Michael Faraday. When he was an apprentice bookbinder in London, the young Faraday read every scientific book that he could find, and since he was particularly fascinated by physics, he managed to obtain a post as laboratory assistant to Humphry Davy, one of the great scientists of the time. After eight years' work he had shown no more than average ability, though he was a competent experimenter. But then, in 1820, Oersted's researches led to the beginning of electromagnetism, and this gave Faraday the chance to show the extent of his genius. Though he began his career as Davy's assistant, he soon overtook him, and finally succeeded him. For a long time Davy was jealous of his one-time assistant, but realised later that 'my greatest discovery was Faraday'.

In this book it is impossible to deal with the whole of Faraday's tremendous achievements. We must omit even his fundamental contribution to the study of the chemical effects of electric currents, and it must suffice here to refer to only two of his discoveries. He was the first to produce an electric current by using magnetism,

thereby observing what may be called the 'symmetrical pheno-menon' to that discovered by Oersted, and finally establishing the link between electricity and magnetism. 28 October 1831, the day on which Faraday made an electric current flow by rotating a copper disk between the poles of a magnet, is an important date in the history of our civilisation. It marked the end of the era of costly and cumbersome Voltaic generators; indeed, Faraday's machine was the ancestor of the modern electric power-station.

In spite of all his practical achievements, Faraday's theoretical work was even more important. Faced with the task of providing a logical skeleton to this new and complex science of eletromagnet-ism, he managed to produce a remarkably simple and extensive interpretation of the phenomena which he observed – even though his knowledge of mathematics was frankly rudimentary. It is diffi-cult to know the extent to which he realised the revolutionary aspect of his way of thinking, but at least his intuition led him to put forward a new conception of the world which was different from Newton's, even though not completely opposed to it. The field concept arose from his explanation of the meaning of *lines of force*.

Lines of force had been under discussion for a long time, because the idea of them had been suggested by a very simple experiment. Place a bar magnet on a table, cover it with a sheet of paper, and then sprinkle some iron filings on the paper. As can be seen from figure 3, the filings do not fall at random, but arrange themselves along regular lines which pass through the poles of the magnet. In other words, the filings fall along the lines of force.

Gilbert had known about this phenomenon, and by Faraday's time it was reasonably well understood. If an experimental subject – in this case, a very small magnet – is placed somewhere on the paper, its effect will be observed along the line of force. It had also been noted that the *density* of the lines of force varied from point to

3 (a) The magnetic field
of a bar magnet, and
(b) the lines of force of
two repelling magnets.

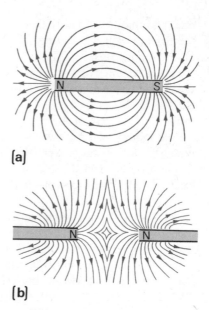

(a)

(b)

4 (a) The lines of force of an isolated electric charge, and
(b) the lines of force of two electric charges of the same polarity.

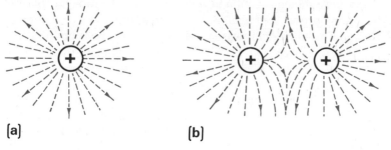

(a)   (b)

point, so that presumably this was an indication of the *intensity* of the force which was acting on the experimental object placed in different positions.

Similarly, lines of force can be drawn for an electric field. The situation for one positive charge and for two identical positive charges is shown in figure 4. The significance of these lines is the same as in the case of the bar magnet, though of course the experimental object will be a weak electric charge instead of a small magnet. Notice, moreover, that because of the analogy between Coulomb's law and the law of gravitation, the lines of force of an electric charge are the same as the gravitational lines of force for a point source of mass.

All this had been known before Faraday's time, and mathematicians such as Green and Gauss had already put forward a complete theory for lines of force. Yet to the earlier workers, the lines were abstract geometrical entities, whose only significance was to show the interactions between material bodies. Newton's ideas still prevailed; space was still regarded as empty except for these particular points, and the interactions between bodies were thought to be propagated instantaneously.

Faraday, on the other hand, reasoned that these lines of force had a physical reality. His intuition had never fully accepted the idea of instantaneous action at a distance, and he thought that the forces were propagated from one point to another at a certain finite velocity. This conviction was strengthened when he found that the force acting between two electric charges – and hence, their mutual energy – is modified if an object such as a sheet of glass is placed between them. He began to regard the lines of force as being real, perhaps the paths taken by energy when dispersed in space. This led to the idea that the electric or magnetic energy is not found in the actual bodies, but in the lines of force themselves, in fact, in the space surrounding the bodies. He filled Newton's empty space with energy distributed along the lines of force, and he substituted the revolutionary concept of the *field* for the Newtonian concept of force acting instantaneously at a distance. The field would be the carrier of energy, and it would be propagated from place to place at finite velocity.

Faraday's concept of the field was something more than mere speculation, because it allowed him to find his way around the complicated maze of electromagnetic phenomena. In a relatively simple manner, he explained some of the most obscure analogies and properties that had baffled his predecessors. More will be said later about this theory of the field. But before continuing its history, it will be helpful to try to arrive at the concept of the field in another way, this time by discussing theories about light.

Fiat Lux

Among the founders of modern science, the Dutchman, Christiaan Huygens, must be considered alongside men such as Galileo and Newton. As a mathematician, he was one of the founders of the theory of probability. As a physicist, he discovered the laws of centrifugal force, and created the theory of the pendulum and of elastic collisions. As an astronomer, he was the first to discover the rings of Saturn and to observe the Great Nebula in Orion. As a technician, he revolutionised the clock industry by introducing the pendulum. His list of achievements is indeed long, but for our present purpose only one need be considered – his contribution to the science of optics.

Although Robert Hooke led the way, Huygens must undoubtedly be regarded as the founder of the *wave theory of light*. When he began his work, the corpuscular theory of light was universally accepted. Light was thought to consist of a stream of small solid particles moving along the direction of the ray. Huygens, however, maintained that light carries no matter in its motion, and that it is made up of waves, which take the form of vibrating movements in space, roughly analogous to the swell of the ocean. Nowadays the idea of light-waves is familiar enough, because radio has been developed, and words such as 'frequency' and 'wavelength' are part of our everyday language. But it may be helpful to pause in order to consider the exact meanings of the terms.

Observe what happens when a stone is dropped into a pool of calm water. Circular waves are produced, spreading outward from the point of impact of the stone, and the waves extend rapidly until they cover the whole of the liquid surface. Therefore, it is clear that the waves *propagate* at a certain speed; but it is not so obvious that the matter (in this case, the water) undergoes no lateral change in position. This can be demonstrated by floating a cork on the water. The cork will bob up and down with the vertical motion of the waves, but it will not move either toward or away from the point of impact of the stone. The propagation of the wave is not a propagation of material, and it follows that the motion of the wave carries energy rather than matter. Thus, the waves on the water carry the energy which makes the cork bob up and down, and on a larger scale is capable of making a boat behave in much the same way.

This oscillation suggests that the wave phenomenon is periodic. If the *period* **T** of the wave is defined as the interval between two successive instants when the cork occupies the same position, then the *frequency* of the wave, represented by the Greek letter nu (v) will be equal to the number of periods per unit time, and we have the equation:

$$v = \frac{1}{T}$$

The wave is periodic in space as well as in time. By means of photography, it can be shown that the distance between two successive crests or troughs remains the same. This distance is called the *wavelength*, and is denoted by the Greek letter lambda (λ); during a period **T**, the wave advances by a length λ. If the velocity of propagation is taken as **v**, we obtain the fundamental relation:

$$\lambda = vT$$

These two equations mean that once the velocity of propagation of a wave is known, its frequency, period and wavelength can also be found. It is quite in order to say that a radio station transmits, say, 'on 50 metres' or 'at 6 megacycles' (6 million periods per second), since the product of these two values works out at 300,000 km/sec, which is the velocity of propagation of Hertzian waves.

Two more characteristics of a wave need to be defined. The first is its *amplitude*, which equals half the vertical distance between the bottom of a trough and the crest of a wave. In the case of waves on water, the amplitude is half of what is commonly called the height of the wave.

The second characteristic, the *phase*, is more difficult to visualise, and it will be helpful to return to the case of the moving cork. This time, however, *two* stones are dropped into the pool, at the same instant but in different positions (see figure 6). The circular waves move out from the points of impact, and the cork starts to bob up and down once more as soon as the waves reach it. The question is to decide whether the oscillation will be of greater or smaller amplitude than was the case when only one stone was dropped into the water. Actually, either can happen, and this is where the idea of *phase* comes into the discussion.

5 Below (a) The shape of a regular wave of amplitude **A** and wavelength λ at a given instant in time.
The wave is travelling from left to right with a velocity **v**.
(b) The same wave superimposed at a time later by **t**. The points originally at S_1, S_2, S_3 . . . have moved a distance **vt** and are now at S'_1, S'_2, S'_3 . . . After a time **T** (the period of the wave), the points S_1, S_2, S_3 . . . will have travelled a distance $vT = \lambda$ and S'_1 will have moved to S_2, S'_2 to S_3, . . . and the wave will have regained its original form.

6 Right Interference of waves caused by the fall of two pebbles.
The circles drawn as solid lines represent the crests of waves at the instant of observation and the dotted circles represent the troughs.
The locus of the points, where one of the waves has the same phase advance as the other, is a hyperbola having C_1 and C_2 as its foci.
On one hyperbola the phase difference is 3 λ, the waves are in phase, and the points **H** are the crests of the resulting wave, while the points **B** are its troughs. On the other hyperbola the phase difference is $5 \cdot 5 \lambda$ and so the waves are in antiphase and the water level is unaffected.

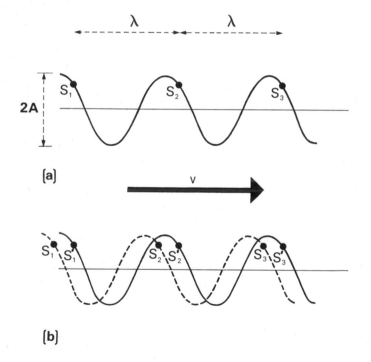

(a)

(b)

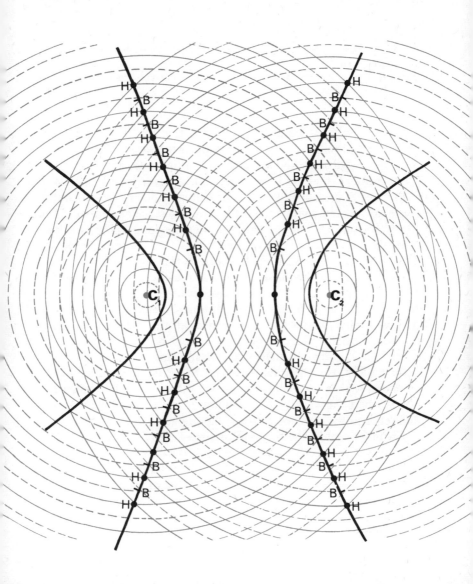

7 Top Photograph of a wave pattern formed by two floats bobbing at the same frequency.
Bottom The wave pattern formed by two floats bobbing at different frequencies: the hyperbolas are damped.

For the sake of simplicity, suppose that the two stones are identical, and that they are dropped from the same height, so that their waves will have the same period, amplitude, and velocity of propagation. If the cork is so placed that it receives the first crest of each wave at the same time, then it will continue to receive all the crests at the same times and all the troughs at the same times. The effects will add up, and the oscillation of the cork will be twice the value that it had in the case of the single stone. On the other hand, if the first wave-crest reaches the cork at the same moment as the trough of a wave from the second stone, the effects of the two waves will be in opposition. Since we have assumed that the waves are equal in every way, there will be a complete cancelling-out, and the cork will remain motionless. Of course, all the intermediate situations are equally likely to occur, but for the moment it will be enough to consider only these two extreme ones.

In the first case the waves are said to be *in phase*, while in the second case they are *in opposite phase*. What, then, determines the points where the waves will or will not be in phase? Obviously, the difference in the distance between the impact points of the stones, or, in other words, the time-lag or time-lead of one of the waves with respect to the other when they reach the cork.

The superposition of two or more waves is known as *interference*, and it is this which explains why it is possible to produce vibrations either greater or smaller than those of the individual waves concerned. In the same way, two sound waves can result in either a more intense or a less intense sound, or even absolute silence, a

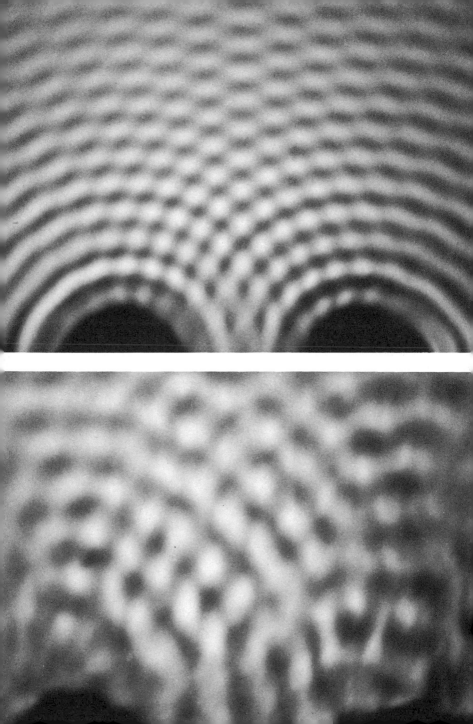

phenomenon well known in some concert halls where there are some positions from which the music is practically inaudible.

Having discussed the fundamental properties of waves, it is time to return to the theory of light. If Huygens were correct in believing light to be a wave-motion, then this strange property of interference would be applicable to optics: two sources might produce either light of greater intensity, or else, alternatively, darkness.

Newton had discovered a phenomenon of this sort (the famous Newton's Rings), but at the time nobody thought about interpreting it by means of wave theory. On the other hand, the existence of different colours is interpreted in the emission theory as different particles for different colours, and Huygens did not know how to explain this. This is why Newton, after hesitating between the two concepts, finally came down on the side of the corpuscular theory. It was of course difficult for him to be totally unbiased when there was such an obvious analogy between the 'particles of light' in the corpuscular idea and the 'particles of matter' in his own mechanics. The wave theory of light was generally abandoned, and Huygens' work was more or less forgotten.

At the beginning of the nineteenth century, a young English scientist, Thomas Young, tried to revive the wave theory, as a result of a practical experiment. Well away from a source of light, he placed a screen in which two pinholes had been pierced very close beside each other. When the light passed through the two holes, two point sources of light were produced, and were made to illuminate a second screen placed behind the first. Young found that the illumination pattern on the second screen was uneven; it was made up of alternate bright and dark *fringes*. As soon as one hole was covered up, the illumination became uniform.

At once Young saw that he had found a decisive argument in favour of the wave theory of light. If the dark strips were present only when both the pinholes were acting as light sources, it was clear that light added to light could produce darkness – and to explain this by means of the corpuscular theory would mean that the particles of light would have to have some very strange properties indeed. If, however, it is assumed that light is a wave motion, then there is a perfect analogy with the two stones and the cork: the light-waves from the two pinholes would *interfere* with each other. If they are in phase when they reach the second screen, they will add up and produce an increase in the intensity of the light; if they are in opposite phase, then they will cancel out, and a dark strip will result.

Young's experiment seemed so simple and convincing that he was confident of having obtained a complete proof of the wave theory of light. Unfortunately, he was a medical doctor rather than a physicist. His published report lacked scientific precision, and his opponents were able to find loopholes in it which Young was unable to counter.

However, it was not long before the wave theory came into its own, largely because of the persistence of Augustin Fresnel, who was a skilful experimenter as well as an excellent mathematician. Although tuberculosis and mental strain shortened his life, he was able to take all the various pieces of information available and to lay the foundations of the modern wave theory of light. He first explained the straight-line propagation, as well as the reasons for the shadow phenomenon, and then proved that these effects are not so absolute as they would have to be on the basis of the corpuscular theory. According to Fresnel, the phenomenon of *diffraction* can make light change its path when it comes to an obstacle. Finally, he was able to explain even the more apparently paradoxical predictions of his theory, and to create the mathematics of wave optics.

During the decades following Fresnel's death in 1827 his theory

8 Below In this modern Young's experiment, a neon-helium gas laser illuminates two slits 0·08 mm wide and 0·64 mm apart.
Right A characteristic diffraction pattern is observed on the screen behind.

was developed and perfected, but one fundamental problem still remained: what is the medium in which these luminous vibrations – the light-waves – propagate? Since light can be propagated through empty space as well as through matter, scientists concluded that there must be a medium which became known as the *luminous ether*, which pervaded all space. Light-waves were assumed to be elastic vibrations of this ether. By studying the properties of light, attempts were made to find out something about the properties of the ether, but the results were in hopeless disagreement,

9 Some great men of classical physics

Top row

Left Isaac Newton (1642–1727). He expressed mathematically the laws of motion and gravitation, and favoured the corpuscular theory of light.
Middle Thomas Young (1773–1823). He proposed the principle of the interference of two wave trains as an explanation of Newton's rings and of the colours of thin films. His work revived the wave theory of light.
Right Michael Faraday (1791–1867). A remarkable scientist who was self-taught, Faraday made many valuable discoveries, particularly in the field of electricity and magnetism.

Bottom row

Left Augustin Fresnel (1788–1827). The wave theory of light gained acceptance largely because of the work of Fresnel who, unlike Young, was a mathematician.
Middle James Clerk Maxwell (1831–1879). His greatest contribution was to formulate the general equations of the electromagnetic field, which led to the electromagnetic theory of light. His *Treatise on Electricity and Magnetism* ranks with Newton's *Principia* as one of the most important books in all science.
Right William Thomson, Lord Kelvin (1824–1907). He introduced the thermodynamic scale of temperature and the absolute scale. Kelvin was worried by the apparent breakdown of classical physics, and spoke of 'two small dark clouds' that would shake its foundations. Later relativity and quantum theory dispelled these clouds. Of his many applied researches perhaps the best known is his work on the first submarine telegraph cables.

due to his explanation of the stability of Saturn's rings. He undertook the task of translating Faraday's field theory into mathematical terms, and he was able to reduce *all* the laws of electricity and magnetism to a set of equations which were then of a completely new type in physics – the famous *Maxwell's Equations* (1865). Boltzmann was so impressed by the power and beauty of these equations that in his treatise on electromagnetism he added, as a footnote, a quotation from Goethe: 'War es ein Gott der diese Zeichen schrieb?' (Is it a god who has written these signs?)

Maxwell's equations put an end to the concepts of action at a distance and instantaneous forces. The field was now thought to propagate from place to place, carrying the electromagnetic forces. But in order to write his equations, Maxwell had been forced to introduce a new hypothesis, which was a natural consequence of the concept of the field and which led him to the discovery of a surprising new property: the electromagnetic field was propagated in wave form! And then, when he calculated the velocity of these waves *in vacuo*, he found that he arrived at a value of 300,000 km/sec, which is, of course, the velocity of light.

Maxwell did not hesitate to conclude that light-waves are nothing more nor less than electromagnetic vibrations, and he showed that by means of his equations it was possible to deduce all the properties of light that Fresnel had found. Thus, the science of optics became part of the science of electromagnetism, and Fresnel's luminous ether became identical with Faraday's electromagnetic ether.

This grandiose analysis was certainly not greeted without reservation, because it introduced concepts so far removed from those of Newton. It was eventually accepted only when Heinrich Hertz confirmed one of its most striking predictions by producing the so-called Hertzian waves by purely electromagnetic methods, so proving that these waves were exactly of the kind that Maxwell had expected.

At the very end of the nineteenth century, Hendrick Antoon Lorentz proposed a theory of electrons which was based on Maxwell's electromagnetism. This paved the way for the new study of *microphysics*, and proved to be highly successful. From then on, the field theory developed first by Faraday and then by Maxwell was used in the study of the new physics.

Probabilities

Let us now turn to the third great point in the classical conception of matter, the *theory of heat*. It will be shown that the science of probability was firmly established in physics long before it became important in quantum theory.

Physicists were not the first to make use of the laws of chance. During the Renaissance, Italian merchants took out insurance against the loss of their ships, basing their reasoning upon statistics. When, much later, three famous scientists, Pascal, Fermat and Huygens, created the mathematics of probability, they did so because of their interest in gambling rather than physics! In fact, it was not until the appearance of the nineteenth century atomic theories that physical laws were first formulated in terms of probability. These atomic theories must be discussed in this book, but before going any further we must ask an important question: in classical physics, how can we reconcile the strict determinism of mechanics on the one hand with the laws of chance on the other? We shall see that far from being incompatible, the two are often so closely linked that they are complementary to each other.

Consider a system subject to the laws of Newtonian mechanics. In principle, the motion of the system can be given very precisely by these laws alone, but in practice it is necessary to know the forces which are acting on the moving object, as well as the position and velocity at a given instant. Usually, this information is not easy to obtain, partly because of the complex nature of the phenomena and partly because the measurements are hard to make accurately enough. This is where use is made of the laws of chance. Since it is impossible to tell exactly what the motion of the system will be, what has to be done is to work out the probability that one or other particular sort of motion will take place. Of course, the answer obtained from probability theory will be much more reliable if the laws of motion are used as well, as can be demonstrated by an actual example: Place a coin on the edge of a table, and on the floor parallel to the edge of the table draw alternate black and white strips of equal width. Hit the coin, so that it drops to the floor and try to predict the colour of the strip upon which it will fall. To the Laplacian determinist, the answer is straightforward. He will say: 'I know the laws of dynamics, the height of the table, the force of gravity, the width of the strips and the velocity that has been given to the coin. This means that I have enough information to work out the colour of the strip'.

Unfortunately, the information is not complete because the initial velocity of the coin is unknown, and this is enough to prevent the problem from being solved dynamically. In other words, this experiment, so far as we are concerned, is a game of chance. But to estimate the probability of the coin's hitting either colour, the laws of mechanics can be invoked. For example, it can be calculated that the coin will fall on the first strip if its velocity is below, say, 20 cm/sec. Let us assume that the first strip is white. If the velocity is between 20 and 40 cm/sec, it will fall on the second strip, which is black, while if the velocity is between 40 and 60 cm/sec the coin will come down on the third strip, which is of course white, and so on.

10 The coin and probability experiment.

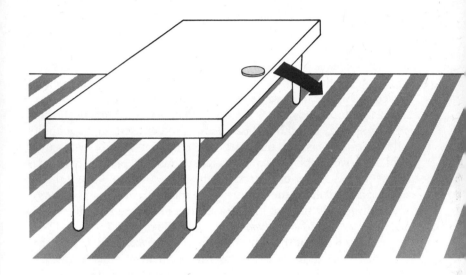

Next, suppose that we have no information whatever about the initial velocity of the coin. We could make up for our lack of knowledge by supposing that there is an equal chance of being in any one of these intervals, so that there is an equal chance of hitting any strip. Since the numbers of white and black strips are equal, it is clear that the probabilities of falling upon either colour are also equal.

The obvious question here is: 'Surely this is the answer which anybody would have reached, so why bother about the laws of mechanics?' The answer is that at least we know *why;* the formula depends upon a precise theory. With further information, the theory can be improved. Suppose, for example, that the initial velocity of the coin is unknown, but is certainly less than 30 cm/sec, so that it has an equal chance of having any value between 0 and 30 cm/sec. What then is the probability that the coin will fall on to a white strip? Instinct will hardly help here, but the laws of mechanics will. The coin is twice as likely to have a velocity between 0 and 20 cm/sec as between 20 and 40 cm/sec, so that it will be twice as likely to fall on the first strip as on the second. Therefore, the chance that the coin will fall on a white strip is 2 to 1 in favour.

This example shows how the laws of chance can come to the help of mechanics, and how mechanics can be used in probability calculations. Classical physicists used this procedure with great skill, and were able to explain a great number of empirical laws about the behaviour of matter. Of these, the two fundamental laws of thermodynamics, the famous principles of *energy* and *entropy*, are undoubtedly the two most basic laws of nature known to man.

The *first law of thermodynamics*, due to Mayer and Joule (1842–3), is the general law of the conservation of energy: energy can neither be created nor destroyed. Energy can occur in various forms, one of which is heat. If, for example, a phenomenon involves only mechanical energy and heat energy, then any loss in mechanical energy (kinetic or potential) will be offset by an equal increase in heat energy; the converse is also true. This is why a thermal motor converts heat into work, while a brake converts work into heat.

It may then be asked whether, if all forms of energy are equivalent, conversion can take place as often as required, so that it would be possible to build a motor whose only source of energy would be the heat in the surrounding air, and slight changes in temperature would keep the motor working. This would be extremely useful, but unfortunately the answer is 'no', because of the *second law of thermodynamics*, discovered by Carnot in 1824. To convert heat into work in a closed cycle, we must have not one source, but two heat-sources at different temperatures. The hotter source must provide the heat energy, of which a part will be transformed into work while the rest will go to the cooler source. Heat cannot travel from a cooler to a hotter body. In a car engine, the combustion of the petrol provides the hot source, while the atmosphere makes up the cool source, and if the engine is not cooled, it will fail just as surely as if it is starved of petrol.

According to this law, there is a grading of the various forms of energy. Energy can drop from one grade to another, but it cannot climb up again, because in all practical cases a part of the energy is always dissipated as heat. Certainly there is a relationship between the work done and the heat produced, but Carnot's principle shows that some of the heat will always be lost, and is not available for re-conversion into work. Therefore, the energy becomes steadily less and less.

Finally, Clausius introduced a new function, entropy, which is fundamental to the whole theory. Entropy may be defined as follows: a source at a temperature of T degrees absolute, which transmits a quantity of heat Q to a body with approximately the same temperature, will transfer an amount of entropy $S = Q/T$. Clausius showed that in accordance with Carnot's principle, the entropy of an *isolated* system must always increase, no matter what phenomena are involved. It follows that since for an isolated system the entropy can never return to its former state, nature must follow an irreversible evolution. This is in agreement with our own subjective impression of the passing of time.

Let us now see how the atomic theory has interpreted these laws. It will be best to take as an example the simplest of the statistical theories, the *kinetic theory of gases*. We can assume that gases are made up of large numbers of molecules, and that the molecules themselves can be regarded as small rigid spheres which obey the laws of classical mechanics. When they collide with each other, or with the walls of their containers, they behave like elastic balls. While there are no collisions, and while no outside forces are acting on the gases, the movement of the molecules is uniform and straight-line, but as soon as a collision occurs this motion is abruptly changed. Actually, the number of collisions is bound to be enormous (of the order of several thousand million per second for each molecule), so that the overall movements are very complicated. They make up what is called *molecular chaos*.

Obviously, mechanics can never give a complete description of the evolution of such chaos, despite the fact that this particular example is relatively simple. The movements of the molecules in a gas make up what may be termed a game of chance, which can be analysed only by statistical methods. There is, in fact, no choice but to accept the results of statistical analysis because the small sizes of the molecules mean that their individual movements cannot possibly be measured. Even the most sensitive apparatus can do no more than measure the mean effects produced by the various movements, or, at best, a few minor deviations from the mean.

The most superficial examination shows the advantages of this concept. Let us imagine that all the molecules of the gas are enclosed in a container. We can alter the volume of the gas, since this involves nothing more than changing the mean distance between the individual molecules; this explains the *expansion* or *compression* of the gas. When a molecule hits a wall of the container, it exerts a force which depends upon its velocity; the force is very slight, but the total effect of these collisions can be large because it is proportional to the mean number of molecules per unit volume. This is known as the gas pressure. Suppose that the volume of the gas is reduced, while the velocity of the molecules remains constant; the number of collisions will then vary inversely with the volume, and so, therefore, will the pressure. In fact, we are doing no more than state the empirical Boyle's law.

It is also possible to increase the velocity of the molecules, and therefore their energy of excitation, without changing the volume of the gas. When this is done, the pressure increases proportionally to the mean of the energy of excitation. But we already know that the pressure is proportional to the absolute temperature of the gas, and this means that the temperature increases in proportion to the mean energy of excitation. In other words, giving heat to a gas in order to increase its temperature comes to the same thing as increasing its molecular energy of excitation, and the heat is in effect converted into a form of mechanical energy. This leads us straight back to the first law of thermodynamics.

However, even in a rigorous form, these arguments did not convince many people, and for a long time the whole atomic theory was regarded with grave suspicion. Few physicists were really interested in the hidden significance of the success of thermodynamics, and were inclined to ask: 'Why bother to re-shape laws based on well-established principles, simply because of some uncertain conclusions drawn from the behaviour of atoms whose very existence is dubious and which, to quote the sarcastic words of a famous mind, "exist only in the dust of libraries"?' The kinetic theory of gases, together with its counterpart, the atomic theory, did not become established for more than eighty years.

And yet some of its results were convincing enough to trouble even the most unresponsive scientific minds. This happened in 1851, when Joule calculated the mean velocity of a molecule of air at normal temperature. He arrived at a figure of between 1,500 and 1,800 km/hour, and this is now known to be correct. But at the time it seemed to be improbably high, and so it was used as an argument against the theory.

11 A very schematic representation of a gas based on the ideas of the kinetic theory.

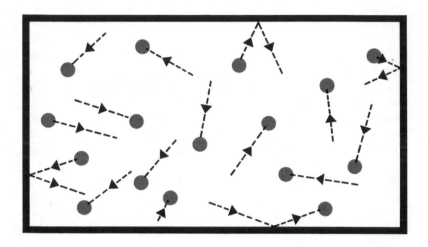

These arguments did not disturb Maxwell's confidence. He went on with his calculations, taking matters much further than Joule, and he next made a decisive discovery with his concept of the *probability of state* of a gas. While he was studying the problems involved in collisions between molecules, Maxwell noted that a collision meant a change in the absolute value of the molecule's velocity as well as a change in direction. If we begin with a gas in which the velocities of all the molecules are equal, collisions will therefore introduce differences in the velocities of the various molecules. The gas will not remain in its original state, and this state must therefore be classed as *improbable*.

Other states, corresponding to various definite re-distributions of the velocities of the molecules, will also be subject to alteration, so that these also will be improbable. Maxwell concluded that the equilibrium state of a gas can correspond only to a *stationary* statistical distribution. Here, the numbers of molecules which lose a given velocity because of collisions are immediately counterbalanced by equal numbers of molecules which gain the same amount of velocity. This is the *most probable* state of a gas, the state which usually occurs. In this way Maxwell introduced the idea of statistical equilibrium, which has proved to be of fundamental importance in many branches of science. He also gave the formula for the distribution of the velocities which lead to this equilibrium for a perfect gas.

This brilliant discovery was of tremendous importance to the whole theory, and it paved the way for the work of Ludwig Boltzmann. While Maxwell had only made calculations with regard to the equilibrium state of a gas, Boltzmann drew up a general equation linking the laws of mechanics to the method of probabilities, and he proved rigorously that a gas will always tend *irreversibly* to the most probable state as calculated by Maxwell. This was significant enough, but the equation brought about an even more important result.

Though the kinetic theory gave an interpretation of the first law of thermodynamics, Carnot's principle did not seem to be another, and the concept of entropy appeared to contradict the laws of mechanics. Boltzmann solved this problem with his celebrated equation, or *H theorem*. This states that a certain function of the probability of the state of the gas decreases steadily with time, and becomes negligible when the gas reaches its state of statistical equilibrium. In other words, the function **H** may be regarded as entropy in the negative sense, hence the term *negentropy* which is sometimes applied to it.

Boltzmann further extrapolated this conclusion in a general principle stating that entropy is only a measure of the probability of the state of a physical system. If so, Carnot's principle means that when a system is away from its state of statistical equilibrium, the probability that it will return to equilibrium is much greater than the probability that it will go the other way. Boltzmann found that the most probable state – thermodynamic equilibrium – corresponds to complete molecular disorder. This is often taken to mean that the universe is tending toward a state of increasing disorder.

This was certainly one of the greatest of all scientific developments. Statistical mechanics, arising from Boltzmann's theory and developed by men such as the great American physicist Josiah Willard Gibbs, has accounted for a great many phenomena, and has led to the theory of quanta. Boltzmann provided ideas which give an impression of the passing of time which causes the ageing of inert matter as well as living matter. The *theory of information* and *cybernetics*, always associated with men such as Wiener, Shannon and Brillouin, is also descended from the work of Boltzmann and Gibbs; it represents a new method of thought in natural science.

Boltzmann was a strange, solitary genius who was generally misunderstood. He committed suicide in the same year that Einstein demonstrated that a well-known phenomenon, Brownian movement, was in complete accord with the kinetic theory. On his tomb, his followers inscribed his famous formula $S = k \log P$, which links entropy with probability, and remains as one of the clues to our understanding of the universe. Certainly it makes a fitting epitaph for Ludwig Boltzmann.

2 Quanta take over physics

2 Quanta take over physics

The end of classical physics

In the last chapter, we have given a review of classical physics. We have described its remarkable success, the way in which it seemed to explain everything, and the absolute confidence that it inspired. The two revolutions that jolted physics at the beginning of the twentieth century were therefore among the greatest upheavals in the history of human thought.

The reception given to Einstein's theory of relativity in 1905 was just as unfavourable as had been the case five years earlier with Planck's hypothesis of quanta. Under the pretext of dissipating Lord Kelvin's 'two little dark clouds', Planck and Einstein between them threw overboard so many firmly-established ideas that they were greeted with scepticism and hostility.

Although the two revolutions have points in common, they are not entirely analogous. Relativity introduced much that was new, but it was still firmly based upon classical physics, and so scientists soon became used to it. Quanta, on the other hand, have always retained a great part of their strangeness.

The theory of relativity, which is not dealt with in the present book, was the result of a clash between the concepts of space and time in Newtonian mechanics on the one hand, and the electromagnetic field theory of Faraday and Maxwell on the other. Einstein showed that the disagreement could be overcome by rejecting the Newtonian concept of absolute time and space, and replacing it by a more elaborate definition which he used as the basis for relativity theory.

Since the theory represented a decisive link between the two major branches of classical physics, mechanics and electromagnetism, its initially unfavourable reception was of no real importance. Einstein (and with him, a growing number of physicists) knew that his point of view was bound to prevail eventually. He was right. Within a few years, what was generally called 'classical mechanics' included relativity; the 'new' mechanics was in effect quantum mechanics.

Its origin was quite unspectacular, and came about, more or less by chance, from the study of a problem which was certainly important, but highly specialised: the so-called *black-body* problem. The quantum theory was a somewhat bizarre hypothesis that had no connection with classical physics or with any other basic principle. As Max Planck, its originator, was to say later, it was a fortunate guess.

Planck was already well-known by the time he put forward his idea of quanta. He was a student under Helmholtz and Kirchhoff, and at the age of thirty-one was appointed to the chair of physics at the University of Berlin, one of the most celebrated universities of the time. His reputation was founded mainly on his brilliant research on the theory of heat, and in particular on his ideas about entropy, which are very close to modern views. Yet there was nothing to forecast that this highly respectable professor would introduce a strange new hypothesis into physics – a hypothesis that nobody much liked, and that most people hoped to be able to discard, but which nevertheless became so firmly established that within a quarter of a century it had led to a recasting of the whole of physics.

First discussions about quanta

In the middle of the nineteenth century, physicists became interested in the way in which bodies emit light when they are heated and absorb heat when they are illuminated. It was particularly instructive to study a body which is capable of absorbing all the radiations, whatever their frequency and hence – for visible light – whatever their colour. A body of this kind is known as a *black body*. The best way to explain what is meant is to suppose that we are looking through a small hole in an oven. Any light entering the hole will be reflected a great many times, and eventually the walls will absorb the whole of the light before it has enough time to come out again.

Now suppose that we heat the oven up to a certain temperature, to 1000°C, for example. Toward the interior, the walls will emit all types of radiations; visible light, infra-red, ultra-violet, and so on. All these will be reflected off the walls, and will eventually be absorbed, but other radiations will be emitted to compensate for them, and the result will be a kind of equilibrium between absorption and emission. The oven will then contain a certain density of radiation – that is to say, electromagnetic waves covering a wide range of frequencies and an equally wide range in intensity.

As we have seen, the hole bored in the side of the oven will absorb all the radiations entering from the outside, but part of the radiation produced inside the oven will be able to escape, and can be studied without difficulty; it has been given the picturesque name of *black-body radiation*. It may be analysed by means of a spectrograph, and we can then find out the different wavelengths and intensities of the different radiations of which it is composed.

The results of these measurements are given in figure 12a, where the wavelengths λ are plotted on the horizontal axis, while the corresponding intensities are given on the vertical axis. The curve shows that the radiations shut inside the oven extend effectively over all wavelengths, but that the relative intensity varies considerably. The intensity is very weak for short wavelengths or ultra-violet radiation. It increases regularly until reaching a maximum at a definite wavelength λ_m, after which it again drops off, becoming very feeble once more in the infra-red range or long wavelength.

The maximum wavelength λ_m is easily found, because it

12 The ultra-violet catastrophe.
(a) The distribution of intensity **(I)** of light
of different wavelengths (λ) emitted by a black body.
(b) According to the classical theories, the intensity
is greatest at very short wavelengths —
that is, in the ultra-violet region.

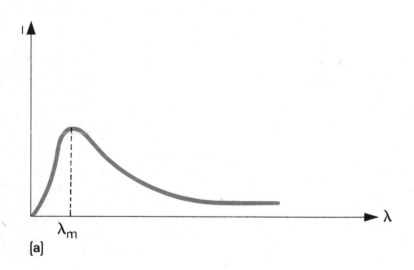

(a)

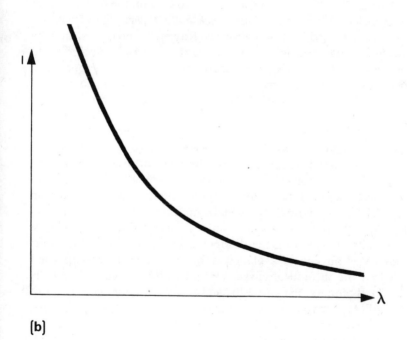

(b)

corresponds to the overall colour of the light coming out of the oven. At 1,000°C, for example, the colour will be red. If we cool the oven down, the curve will be altered so that the maximum point λ_m will be shifted to the right, and the colour will change to darker red. If the oven is heated up, the point λ_m will be shifted toward the left.

These experimental results were well known in the last century, and around 1880 an attempt was made to explain them on the basis of the classical theories. This *black-body theory* was developed essentially by the British physicists Rayleigh and Jeans, and by Kirchhoff and Wien in Germany. Light was treated according to the Maxwell-Lorentz electromagnetic theory, and was supposed to be emitted or absorbed by electrons which oscillated in conformity with the laws of Newtonian mechanics. The equilibrium between emission and absorption was then calculated from Boltzmann's statistical theorem.

Unfortunately, it was clear that at least one of the three theories must be incorrect, because the results were in disagreement with practical observation. The curve shown in figure 12b is derived from theoretical considerations, and is quite different from the curve in figure 12a, which was obtained from practical experimentation. Although the two curves were similar for large values of λ (that is, in the infra-red region), the discrepancy for the short, ultra-violet region was obvious at a glance. What was even more important was that the theoretical curve was not only inexact, but actually absurd. If the curve in figure 12b had been correct, the total energy of the radiation contained inside the oven would have to be infinite.

It is easy to appreciate that these results came as a disagreeable surprise. Classical physics was so firmly founded that this 'ultra-violet catastrophy', as it came to be called, shook the whole edifice. The black-body theory was checked and rechecked, but the results were always the same: the ultra-violet catastrophy was the inevitable consequence of adhering to the great classical principles. Evidently it was not without reason that the inquiring mind of Lord Kelvin had been apprehensive about the first of his 'little dark clouds'.

Then, in December 1900, Max Planck put before the Academy of Sciences in Berlin his fourteenth memoir on the black-body theory. It was this memoir which later became so famous, because in it Planck proposed the addition of a new concept to classical physics – the *quantum hypothesis*. With this addition, the ultra-violet catastrophe could be solved, experimental results and theory could be made to agree, and the black-body theory fell neatly into place.

The solution seemed to be ideal, but it was not received with any real enthusiasm, and even Planck himself proposed it as merely a temporary expedient. However, before discussing the reasons for the chilly reception given to the theory, something must be said about this idea of quanta, which has played such a major role in science. To avoid any misunderstanding, it will be best to use an example which has nothing to do with black-body radiation.

Take a certain quantity of water and weigh it. The result may be expressed as a number – 20 kg, for example. By adding or subtracting water, we can alter this number, and since we can add or subtract very small quantities of water, this alteration can be made as small as is desired, whatever may be the initial quantity of water. In a case such as this, the weight of a quantity of water is said to be a *continuous* parameter – on the scale used in everyday experience.

Next, consider a load of bricks. Again the total weight may be expressed as a certain number, which can be altered by changing the number of bricks, but the variation will be different from the case of the water, because each change will be in terms of an arbitrarily small quantity. If, for example, each brick weighs 2 kg, the overall weight of the load can be altered by 2 kg or multiples of 2 kg, but not by any other amount. For this reason, the weight of the load of bricks is called a *discontinuous* parameter, and the smallest variation of the parameter is known as the *quantum of weight*. In our present example, the quantum will, of course, be the weight of one brick.

Using this new terminology, we can now return to the problem of black-body radiation. Classical physics implies that the absorption and emission of light by matter must be continuous processes, so that the quantity of luminous energy emitted or absorbed in a certain time-interval (one second, for instance) by the wall of the oven can be varied by as little as desired. We can even go down in scale, and consider the emission from a single atom of the wall. In other words, classical physics regards light as behaving in the manner of a flowing liquid, so that its quantity can be changed at will. In particular, since the energy of a wave depends solely upon its amplitude, this amplitude must be a continuous parameter.

It was in straight contradiction to these well-established ideas that Planck put forward his new theory, according to which *the emission of luminous energy by an atom of matter can occur only in a discontinuous manner, by quanta*. If the frequency of a wave is v, it must have been emitted by matter with energy which is a multiple of the quantum of energy:

$$E = hv,$$

where **h** is a universal constant, now known as *Planck's constant*.

This idea is familiar enough nowadays, but it sounded very alien in 1900, and it is worth making an attempt to see how a physicist of that time might have regarded it. He might well have thought: 'The idea is ridiculous. If the emission of radiation is a discontinuous process, the amplitude of the waves must also become discontinuous. The electromagnetic theory of light will have to be drastically overhauled, or even abandoned, and this is too great a price to pay even for the solution of the black-body problem'.

And yet our imaginary physicist may have had inner qualms. 'True, if we calculate the value of Planck's constant we are bound to obtain a very small number. The quanta of energy will also be small, and any wave will contain enormous numbers of them, so that for all practical purposes the wave will behave just like a stream of water – which also is discontinuous, because it is made up of atoms, even though the atoms are small enough to make the stream appear continuous. Perhaps the whole idea may not be so absurd after all'.

So far, so good, but the physicist might soon recover from this temporary weakness: 'But this is evading the problem, and the whole question is one of principle. Even though the discontinuity of the luminous wave due to its emission by quanta may be extremely small, it still clashes with the concept of the Faraday-Maxwell field. How can energy which is being sent out in small packets be propagated as a wave-form? After all, electrons oscillate in an atom, and this is why they emit continuous light. The light carries away their energy, so that their oscillation slows down progressively in the same way as a swing which is left to itself. But if the light is emitted by quanta, then the amplitude of the oscillation of the electron will remain unchanged until a quantum is emitted, and then there will be a sudden reduction. Suppose that this argument is applied to the swing: left on its own, its amplitude will remain unchanged until it suddenly loses all its energy and comes to an abrupt halt, instead of slowing down gradually. According to all the evidence, this is unacceptable'.

Doubts of this kind were widely voiced when the quantum theory was first put forward, and even Planck shared them to some extent. He, above all, was in a position to appreciate the difficulties and problems raised by quantum theory, and for some time the whole question remained open.

In the same year, 1900, a young student graduated from the Polytechnic Institute of Zürich. He had not shown any particular ability, and had been noticed only in that he had avoided certain lectures that he regarded as boring. He failed to secure the post of assistant in a university, and ended up by going into the Patent Office in Bern. His name was Albert Einstein.

Five years later, at the time when he put forward the theory of relativity and claimed that mass and energy must be equivalent, Einstein was to discover the existence of these 'particles of light', which today we call *photons*. And at last the idea of quanta became a matter for serious discussion among all physicists.

Light particles and ghost waves

In 1887 Heinrich Hertz was engaged in his famous experiments in connection with radio-electric waves. Quite by chance, he noted that if a piece of zinc were illuminated with ultra-violet light, it became electrically charged. This so-called *photoelectric effect* was soon obtained also with visible light upon various metals and alloys.

The practical consequences of the photoelectric effect are innumerable, because an electric signal can be produced by means of a beam of light. Photographic apparatus and television depend upon it, as do the automatic doors that are opened by means of 'electric eyes'. In this book, however, we must consider not its practical applications, but the more abstract problem of its physical interpretation.

At first sight the photoelectric effect seems interesting, certainly, but also quite easy to understand. If small negative electric charges, that is, electrons, are moving freely inside metals, and if they receive some light (which is only an electromagnetic wave), they will pick up some energy and will become excited. When the excitation has become great enough, it will be natural for the electrons to break free from the forces holding them inside the metal so that they will escape outside. According to classical theory, the greater the energy of the light, the greater the intensity, and the easier it will be for the phenomenon to occur.

At this point the classical physicist will apparently be justified in believing that he is making progress. He has taken some simple ideas, and used them to form the basis of a plausible theory. Unfortunately, however, he is completely wrong.

Take a piece of zinc, and illuminate it with red light. It will be found that whatever the intensity of the light-beam, no electron will ever leave the metal, so that the experiment fails. With light of higher frequency, such as yellow, blue or violet, the result is still negative. The photoelectric effect is obtained only with ultra-violet light, which has a higher frequency still. And at this, the classical physicist has to admit defeat.

Evidently, then, once we have found the type of light able to produce the photoelectric effect, even a very weak beam will suffice. In other words, the ejection of an electron from a metal is dependent not on the intensity of the light, but on its 'colour', and this is quite contrary to classical theory. There seems to be what may be called a 'frequency limit' for each metal; light of lower frequency will produce no photoelectric effect, whatever its intensity, while light of higher frequency will always give rise to the effect even when the intensity is very feeble.

If we now measure the speed at which the electrons leave the metal, another surprising result is found. The greater the frequency of light beyond the 'threshold', the greater the speed of ejection, and here, too, the speed is independent of the intensity of the light-beam.

Intensity does, however, play some role, since it controls the number of electrons ejected from the metal once the process has been started. If the intensity of the light beam is doubled, the number of electrons ejected will also be doubled, though their speeds will not be changed. Clearly, then, it is the frequency and not the intensity of the light that controls the energy given to the electron. Unfortunately for classical theory, wave theory states that the frequency is independent of the energy.

These awkward properties were discovered toward the end of the last century, and scientists tried vainly to solve the difficulty by looking for some mysterious property of metals. Then, in 1905, the young Einstein took a hand. He understood that light, not the metal, was responsible for the phenomena, and he put forward a theory that was even more audacious than Planck's. Despite the universal belief in the Fresnel-Maxwell wave theory of light, he went back to a modified form of the old corpuscular theory of light, which had been supported by Newton but which had long since been abandoned.

While everybody, Planck included, was trying hard to understand the significance of the theory of quantum emission, Einstein went much further, and suggested that *luminous energy is always concentrated in the form of particles*, the light quanta which we now call photons. If so, then a beam of light will behave in the manner of a shower of particles. When the beam falls on a metallic surface, a photon may score a direct hit on an electron, and if the energy is great enough, the electron will be knocked out of the metal.

If this picture is correct, it follows that the ejection of electrons from the metal, in other words, the photoelectric effect, is controlled not by the number of photons, but by the energy of *each* individual photon. The occurrence of the photoelectric effect is related to the frequency of the light-wave, and so it is this frequency that determines the energy of the photon. Einstein next pointed out that there was already a known law connecting frequency with energy, which was Planck's law of quanta, $E = h\nu$. Admittedly, this law was still rather dubious, and restricted to the black-body problem, but Einstein adopted it as a general principle, and assumed that every light-wave of frequency ν carries particles of light each with an individual energy $E = h\nu$.

With these hypotheses, the laws of the photoelectric effect become clear. If the electrons in a metal do not escape naturally, then there must be a certain force holding them back, so that a certain amount of energy E_0. will be needed to overcome this force and eject the electron. For this to happen, a photon will have to possess energy at least equal to E_0. According to Planck's formula, this implies that the frequency of the light-wave carrying the photon will have to be at least equal to the frequency ν_0, defined by the formula

$$E_0 = h\nu_0,$$

It follows that this frequency, ν_0 will be the 'threshold frequency' mentioned above. Next, suppose that the frequency ν of the light is greater than ν_0; the photon will not only be able to eject the electron from the metal, but will give it a certain energy of motion, so that it will be ejected at a certain speed. Its maximal kinetic energy E_{max} will be equal to the energy E of the incident photon minus the energy necessary for the ejection of the electron, thus:

$$E_{max} = E - E_0 = h\nu - h\nu_0$$

Thus the energy increases with the frequency of the incident light, which agrees with observation. Also, this simple formula shows just *how* the energy increases with the frequency, as was also confirmed by practical experiments carried out later.

13 Max Planck (1858–1947) proposed that when atoms emit or
absorb light their energy states change by a discrete amount –
by a quantum of energy.

Next, we must discuss how the intensity of the light controls the
number of electrons liberated. Assume that the frequency of the
wave is greater than the threshold-frequency, so that the energy of
the photons is sufficient to produce the photoelectric effect. Each
of the photons will therefore have a certain probability of colliding
with an electron and knocking it out of the metal. Intuitively, it may
be assumed that if the number of photons in the wave is doubled,
then twice as many electrons will be removed from the metal; the
number of electrons ejected will be in proportion to the number of
photons. To bring this idea into line with the experimental results,
Einstein brought in a second relationship between photons and
waves. He simply assumed that the intensity is proportional to the
number of photons carried by the wave.

It is obvious at once that this definition of intensity, as proposed
by Einstein, is much the same as that given by classical optics. If the
luminous energy is concentrated in the photons, then the total
energy of the wave is the sum of the energies of all the photons
carried. If the frequency is determined, it follows that all the
photons will have the same energy, and the total energy must be
proportional to their number. In classical theory, this energy is
defined by the intensity of the wave. Since Einstein assumed that
the intensity of the wave is proportional to the number of photons,
the two definitions are not mutually contradictory.

All the same, Einstein's revelations caused a major modification
in the theory of light, because when stripped of its energy the
luminous wave becomes what might be called a *ghost wave*. It

14 Albert Einstein (1879–1955) is shown here at the age of 26 working as a clerk in the Swiss Patent Office. It was at this time that he completed the statistical theory of Brownian movement, introduced the quantum explanation of the photoelectric effect and announced the special theory of relativity.

behaves like a *Deus ex machina* controlling the properties of the photons: it is the frequency of the wave which defines the energy of the photons, and the wave-intensity which determines the photon concentration. This leads on to the assumption that the wave is even responsible for guiding the movements of the photons.

Once, again, all the classical ideas were remoulded through the explanation of a single phenomenon. At that time, Einstein wrote to one of his friends: 'I have just published a fundamental paper about light, but I am sure that nobody will understand it.' He was right. Opinion was unanimously against him, and many years passed by before his theory was experimentally verified. By then, however, light-quanta too had been verified, along with the theory of the atom.

Atoms are not indivisible

Atoms have been discussed for at least twenty-five centuries. According to Aristotle, Leucippus of Miletus first referred to them, though his reasons are not known, and may have been pure intuition. Democritus used them as the basis of his cosmogony; they inspired the philosophy of Epicurus and, later, the beautiful philosphical poem written by Lucretius. After that, nothing more was heard about atoms for a very long time.

It was only in the eighteenth century that interest in atoms was revived, with Bernouilli and Lomonosov, who made attempts to use them in physics in connection with the kinetic theory of gases. Yet another fifty years elapsed before John Dalton put forward his atomic theory, which was to become a scientific doctrine with regard to the constitution of matter.

The atoms of classical science, as pictured by Dalton and Boltzmann, were uninteresting enough, since their only properties were volume and mass. They could hardly be called 'atoms' in the modern sense, since they were regarded as indivisible, and it is remarkable that so many natural laws could have been explained on the basis of so few hypotheses. Moreover, the concept of atoms as being indivisible and motionless was not without its difficulties, of which the most important was the periodic classification of elements, discovered almost simultaneously in 1870 by Mendeleyev and Meyer.

Both Mendeleyev and Meyer had the idea of arranging the chemical elements in order of increasing atomic weight so that each element had a definite 'number of order', which corresponds almost exactly with the modern *atomic number*. Hydrogen, the lightest of the atoms, had atomic weight 1, and was arranged first in the series; lithium, atomic weight 7, was placed second, and so on. All the known elements could be fitted into the sequence, and it was found that elements with similar chemical properties appeared in the periodic table at surprisingly regular intervals.

Take, for example, the first three alkali metals, lithium, sodium and potassium. Their atomic numbers are 3, 11 and 19 respectively, so that there is an interval of 8 between each, and they have similar chemical properties. It is found that the three elements immediately following them, beryllium (atomic number 4), manganese (12) and calcium (20), also have chemical properties which resemble each other. The same is true for the three preceding elements, helium, neon and argon.

Actually, the order of the original table was not so straight-forward as this, because elements had to be put into places in the sequence where they did not fit, and the periodicity was largely spoiled. But Mendeleyev and Meyer realised that the periodicity was more important than the weights, and they arranged their table in column form, giving one column to each of the 'families' of elements with similar properties, for example, sodium below lithium, and potassium below sodium. To keep the periodical sequence, they had to leave various blank spaces, each of which was allotted an atomic weight.

They assumed that the blank spaces corresponded to chemical elements which were still unknown. On the basis of the periodic sequence, and taking the properties of the known elements into account, they were able to predict the properties of the unknown elements. They deciphered the world of atoms as one deciphers a foreign language from a scrap of document. As time went by, chemists slowly filled up Mendeleyev's table, and in every case the forecasts were confirmed (see old and modern tables figure 15).

If the existence of atoms is accepted, it can hardly be doubted that the periodicity of the table is due to the structure of these atoms. The discovery of this structure, fifty years later, was a signal victory for quantum theory, but the first steps were actually taken in Mendeleyev's time. Though many physicists still objected to the whole atomic idea, others were already becoming interested in a new 'atom' – the atom of electricity, or *electron*.

In 1859, Plücker was working on the production of electrical dis-charges produced in a glass container filled with rarefied gas. He noticed a green fluorescence on the sides of the container next to the cathode or negative electrode, and he came to the conclusion

Series	Group I R_2O	Group II RO	Group III R_2O_3	Group IV RH_4 RO_2	Group V RH_3 R_2O_5	Group VI RH_2 RO_3	Group VII RH R_2O_7	Group VIII — RO_4	
1	H = 1								
2	Li = 7	Be = 9·4	B = 11	C = 12	N = 14	O = 16	F = 19		
3	Na = 23	Mg = 24	Al = 27·3	Si = 28	P = 31	S = 32	Cl = 35·5		
4	K = 39	Ca = 40	— = **44**	Ti = 48	V = 51	Cr = 52	Mn = 55	Fe = 56 Co = 59 Ni = 59 Cu = 63	
5	(Cu = 63)	Zn = 65	— = **68**	— = **72**	As = 75	Se = 78	Br = 80		
6	Rb = 85	Sr = 87	?Yt = 88	Zr = 90	Nb = 94	Mo = 96	— = 100	Ru = 104 Rh = 104 Pd = 106 Ag = 108	
7	(Ag = 108)	Cd = 112	In = 113	Sn = 118	Sb = 122	Te = 125	I = 127		
8	Cs = 133	Ba = 137	?Di = 138	?Ce = 140	—	—	—	— — —	
9	(—)	—	—	—	—	—	—		
10	—	—	?Er = 178	?La = 180	Ta = 182	W = 184	—	Os = 195 Ir = 197 Pt = 198 Au = 199	
11	(Au = 199)	Hg = 200	Tl = 204	Pb = 207	Bi = 208				
12	—	—	—	Th = 231	—	U = 240	—	— — —	

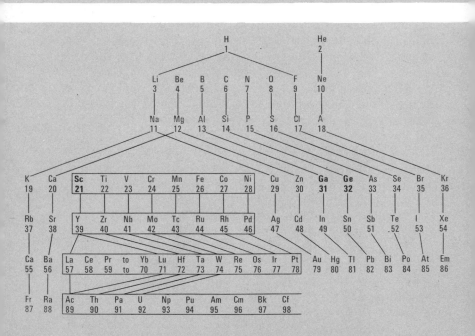

15 Top Mendeleyev's periodic table (1871).
Bottom The modern version according to Thomsen and Bohr.

that this fluorescence must be caused by invisible rays escaping from the cathode. Moreover, he proved that the rays could be deviated by a magnet just like an electric current. They are now known as *cathode rays*.

Plücker's researches were followed up by other investigators, and after much discussion it was assumed that the mysterious rays must be made up of tiny particles of negative electricity which became known as *electrons*. In support of this idea, Helmholtz showed that Faraday's laws of electrolysis could be simply explained by admitting the existence of electrons. All the same, there was no decisive proof, and the whole theory remained highly vulnerable.

Confirmation was finally obtained by Sir Joseph John Thomson. In a series of famous experiments, he not only measured the mass and charge of the electron on the basis of several different physical effects, but also showed that the charge carried by the cathode rays was the same as that carried by Faraday's electrolytic ions. In 1897, physicists were able to announce the discovery of a particle which carried a fixed electric charge, and which was *almost two thousand times lighter than the least massive atom*. In other words, an atom could no longer be regarded as the smallest possible unit of matter.

Another discovery of vital importance had been made in the previous year. While Henri Becquerel had been studying the phenomenon of natural fluorescence – a development of the discovery of x-rays – he had found that the natural salts of uranium continuously send out rays which have a penetrating power far greater than that of x-radiation. Becquerel found that these rays were electrically charged, and were not produced by any outside force. He had discovered *radioactivity*, which indicates that changes can take place within atoms, and also demonstrates instability. In this book we cannot delve deeper into this fruitful discovery, which gave rise to two new sciences, nuclear physics and nuclear chemistry. These latter were, of course, founded by Pierre and Marie Curie, and were followed up later by some of the greatest of modern scientists.

Pride of place must undoubtedly go to Ernest Rutherford. One of his great achievements was to show that radioactivity is the result of the transmutation of one atom to an atom of another kind. It may be described as a sort of explosion, and what Becquerel had done was to observe its effects. But if one chemical element can be transformed into another, it is obvious that the atom must have a definite structure.

By a curious chance, the phenomenon of radioactivity provided not only the means for looking for such a structure, but also gave an actual method of investigating it. What had to be done was to use the radiations sent out by radioactive material. We now know that these radiations are of three different kinds: *alpha* (*a*) *rays*, consisting of nuclei of helium atoms and therefore carrying a positive electric charge; *beta* (*β*) *rays*, made up of electrons moving close to the velocity of light; and *gamma* (*γ*) *rays*, which are of electromagnetic nature, and resemble extremely penetrating x-rays.

All these rays were to play great roles in scientific research. In particular, *γ*-rays are used in the treatment of cancer, while *β*-rays were used originally to show the accuracy of the provisions of special relativity theory. But it was the *a*-rays that physicists were able to use as projectiles to bombard matter and to determine its composition.

16 The three types of radiation emitted by a radioactive source
behave very differently in a magnetic field. The γ rays,
which have no electric charge, are not deviated, but the α and β rays,
which carry charges of opposite sign, are deviated along
paths which curve away from each other. The curvature depends
on the mass and velocity of the particles.

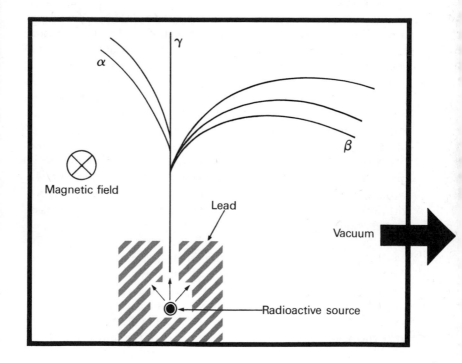

At the beginning of the present century, then, physicists were starting to learn at least something about atomic structure. At the same time investigations were going on with the discharge tubes that had first led to the discovery of electrons. New rays had been found, made up of positively-charged particles such as helium nuclei (a-rays). It was concluded that the electric charges of these new rays were caused by a lack of electrons, and it was assumed that each atom must consist of a combination of electrons and positive charges.

J. J. Thomson then suggested that an atom is made up of a central positive charge surrounded by negative electrons, so that in its normal state it is electrically neutral. Yet, if solid matter is made up of atoms which are joined together, there would be no free space in which to move about, and how could the electrons of cathode rays pass through solid material? It was even more difficult to see how a-rays, which are themselves 'atoms', could move in almost straight lines through a thickness of material containing a hundred thousand atoms. Yet the a-rays could, and did, behave in such a manner. In Thomson's model, solid matter would resemble a thick bush, while a sheet of matter would be a kind of bushy hedge. The effect of throwing an a-particle at matter would then be equivalent to throwing a football against a hedge – with luck, it might penetrate some way in but it could never pass right through.

In 1901, Jean Perrin put forward the correct hypothesis. He regarded an atom as a miniature Solar System, in which the planetary electrons moved round a tiny positive 'sun' at distances which were very great relative to the diameters of the particles. Later, Perrin's central 'sun' was christened the *nucleus* of the atom. If we construct a model of an atom as we know it today, and if we make the whole atom occupy a space equal to the dimensions of a big town, then the nucleus and each of the electrons will be about the size of an orange; all the rest of the atom will be empty space. In other words, the material of the atom is concentrated in a very small part of the total volume, and because the electrons are extremely light, it follows that nearly all the mass of the atom is contained in the nucleus.

When it is said that atoms of solid material are joined, what is really meant is that the outermost electrons of each atom are close to the outermost electrons of the adjacent atoms, so that even the densest solid will be made up chiefly of empty space. With this model, matter no longer resembles a bush, and a sheet of material may be compared not with a hedge, but with a row of trees. If we throw a football against the row of trees, or in our example, an a-particle against a sheet of material, there is every chance of it passing through in a straight line, though sometimes one of the 'trees' will be struck and the projectile will be deflected.

This was exactly the phenomenon which had been observed by Rutherford in 1911, when he noticed that in crossing a thin sheet of material some of the a-particles were deflected as though they had met some heavy obstacle. Rutherford remembered the planetary model of the atom; and wondered if it could be the atomic particles which were deflecting the a-particles? He worked out a general equation for the flow of charged particles across a definite thickness of material, predicting the proportion of particles which should be deflected by a given amount. He tested his calculations experimentally and obtained results which were so convincing that henceforth the planetary theory of the atom was universally accepted by all research workers.

However, the problem of atomic structure was by no means solved. Once again classical physics proved to be inadequate, and had to give way to the theory of quanta.

84

17 When Rutherford bombarded a gold foil with α particles from a radium source, the particles that passed through the foil produced a flash of light on a fluorescent screen behind. That nearly all the α particles went right through or suffered only small deflections indicated that the atom was mainly empty space. Some particles, however, were deflected through large angles and Rutherford deduced that the atom had a small, massive core, the nucleus.

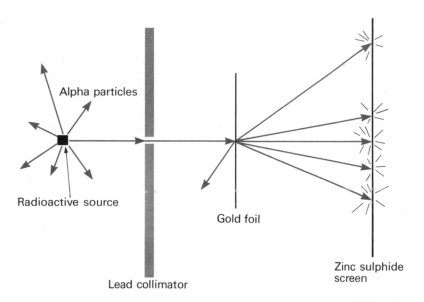

Alpha particles

Radioactive source

Lead collimator

Gold foil

Zinc sulphide screen

A quantised solar system

Around 1912 the atomic theory was really coming into its own. It was then, too, that a young Danish physicist named Niels Bohr came to Manchester to work in Rutherford's laboratory. Atomic theory was being found to be in accord with countless older experiments, drawn from chemistry, electricity, thermodynamics and even from the forms of crystals and the blue colour of the sky. Indeed, the idea of atoms had become so well established that Poincaré had said: 'Now that we know how to count them, we almost imagine that we can see them.'

On the other hand, it had to be admitted that ideas about atomic structure were still vague and contradictory. It was true that Rutherford's experiments confirmed the idea of an atom as a miniature Solar System, but the remarkable stability of an atom was very hard to understand. According to the Maxwell-Lorentz theory, all electric charges that are not moving uniformly in a straight line must be radiating light constantly. As this would apply to the planetary electrons, they would presumably lose their energy and would end up by falling into the nucleus. According to classical physics, Rutherford's results were impossible, and classical physics would therefore have to be changed.

Bohr saw that there must be a link between this new mystery and the old, highly respectable study of *spectroscopy*, which had been born when Newton had used a glass prism to split up white light into all the colours of the rainbow. Unlike his contemporaries, Newton had maintained that the colours of the *spectrum* were inherent in light itself, and were not merely created by the prism. The true explanation was given much later by Young, who made use of the wave theory, and assumed that white light is made up of a mixture of waves with different frequencies, so that the various waves were deflected by different amounts in passing through the prism, depending on their frequency. In physics, it is always so difficult to introduce novel ideas that this explanation was rejected because of the corpuscular theory of light, whose greatest advocate had been Newton himself.

The founders of modern spectroscopy were Bunsen and Kirchhoff, both of whom were professors at the University of Heidelberg, and whose friendship was to prove of the greatest profit to physics. Fraunhofer had found that optical spectra contained mysterious lines which we now call *spectral lines*. Bunsen and Kirchhoff proved that the frequencies of these lines depend on the characteristics of the body emitting them, and that the lines could be used to identify the various chemical elements. By such methods they were able to examine the chemical compositions of the stars, an undertaking which had previously been regarded as impossible.

From that moment interest in spectroscopic studies grew steadily. Eventually it was found that there was a certain regularity in the dispositions of the spectral lines, and it was possible to work out definite arrangements in the form of groups. At the end of the nineteenth century, the Swiss physicist Balmer, who devoted almost a lifetime's work to the problem, was able to give a simple formula which expressed all the spectral frequencies of the visible light of hydrogen:

$$\nu = \frac{Rc}{4} - \frac{Rc}{n^2}$$

in which **c** is the velocity of light and **R** a constant now known as *Rydberg's Constant*. By giving **n** successive values of 3, 4, 5 and so on, Balmer was able to express the observed frequencies with complete accuracy.

This first numerical law of spectroscopy quickly led on to others.

18 A freehand sketch by Newton of one of his experiments on colour. He first split light into a spectrum with a large prism and then allowed light of a single colour to pass through a hole in a screen to a second prism. This did not produce more colours. He also found that a second prism placed in the spectrum would recombine the colours into white. Thus white light is made up of all the colours of the spectrum. The modern spectroscope is just a technical improvement on Newton's.

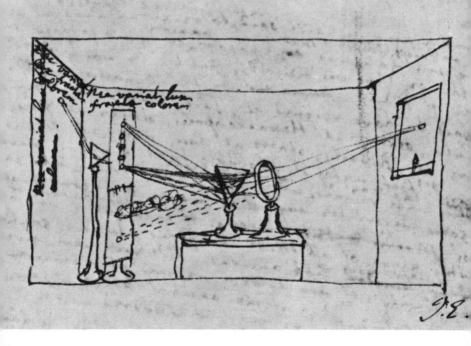

19 In his thesis, de Broglie showed that the orbits postulated
by Bohr for the electron rotating around the core of the
hydrogen atom could be deduced by imposing the restriction that
the length of the orbits must contain a whole number of
wavelengths of the electron, given by $\lambda = h/\,mv$.
In **(a)**, **(b)** and **(c)** this condition is satisfied for n = 2, 4 and 8
respectively. In **(d)** the rule is broken and the unstable motion
leads to the self-destruction of the wave through interference.

A general form is:

$$v = \frac{Rc}{m^2} - \frac{Rc}{n^2}$$

where $\mathbf{m} = 1, 2, 3, \ldots$ and $\mathbf{n} = \mathbf{m} + 1, \mathbf{m} + 2, \mathbf{m} + 3 \ldots$ and so
on. This gives the spectral frequencies of hydrogen not only in the
visible range, but also in the infra-red and the ultra-violet. Then, in
1908, Ritz arrived at a general principle: for each atom, it is
possible to find a series of numbers N_1, N_2, N_3 ... called *spectral
terms*, such that all frequencies of the spectrum of the atom can be
expressed as the difference $N_m - N_n$ between two of these spectral
terms.

These were the great empirical laws of spectroscopy, but all
tentative attempts at theoretical explanation came up against a
blank wall. According to classical theory, light emitted by atoms
must contain all frequencies at the same time. The existence of
spectral lines could not be accounted for, and the Balmer and Ritz
laws were even more puzzling.

Faced with the double enigma of the stability of planetary atoms
and the emission of spectral lines, Bohr had the courage to reject
the laws of classical physics and to look for new laws which might
be more effective and more signficant. His initial step was perhaps
rather naïve. He set out to keep Rutherford's model, and added to

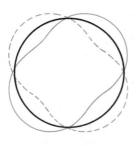

(a) Circumference = 2 Wavelengths

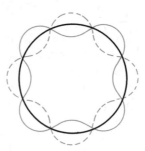

(b) Circumference = 4 Wavelengths

(c) Circumference = 8 Wavelengths

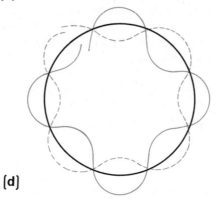

(d)

it the spectral emission of light, basing his outlook upon quantum theory. Yet the elegance and simplicity of the solution he proposed showed a flash of genius.

If light is emitted and absorbed by quanta, then one has to suppose, as Planck had had to do for his oscillators, that an atom can exist only in certain particular states which correspond to a series of values of increasing energy E_1, E_2, E_3, etc. The emission or absorption of a photon is the result of a transition between two of these states. Let us imagine that an atom in a state of energy E_m suddenly changes into a state of lesser energy E_n. Assuming that the general principle of the conservation of energy is valid, then the energy lost by the atom in this *quantum jump* is given to the photon which is emitted. The energy of the photon will therefore be $h\nu = E_m - E_n$, so that the frequency of the light emitted by the transition must be written as

$$\nu = \frac{E_m}{h} - \frac{E_n}{h}$$

This is certainly a remarkable result. Applying the quantum hypothesis to the atom, Bohr deduced that all the emission and absorption frequencies of the light could be given in the form of the difference between two values taken from a discontinuous sequence. In other words, all that he had to do to recreate Ritz' general law was to write it down in the form

$$N_k = \frac{E_k}{h}$$

Yet although success seemed very possible, it was not certain. This astonishing interpretation of Ritz' formula could be put down to pure chance, unless the empirical values of the spectral terms could be found exactly. Obviously the calculations would be very complicated, but in the case of the hydrogen atom, with its one electron moving round the central nucleus, it might perhaps be done. Therefore, everything depended upon Balmer's formula.

Consider an electron moving round a nucleus, and suppose, for the sake of simplicity, that its orbit is circular. According to classical mechanics, this orbit can have any radius, and each of these radii must correspond to a specified energy. The problem comes down to making a selection from all the possible motions so that the energies E_1, E_2 ... E_n will give exact values of the spectral terms in agreement with Balmer's formula.

To an orthodox physicist, this selection of a few definite radii must have seemed little short of sacrilege. Yet it was in accord with quantum theory, and, after all, Planck had done much the same thing with his oscillators. The young Danish scientist did not hesitate. Very well, to separate the wheat from the chaff in the multitude of classical movements, he decided to apply the same sort of rule that had brough success to Planck.

The result of his calculations seemed almost miraculous. Bohr found that the frequencies of all the spectral lines of hydrogen could be expressed by the general formula

$$\nu = \frac{2\pi^2\,Me^4}{h^3}\;\left(\frac{1}{m^2} - \frac{1}{n^2}\right)$$

where **m** and **n** are whole numbers, **e** and **M** are the charge and mass of the electron, **h** is Planck's constant, and π has the value of 3·14. Defining the constant **R** by

$$R = \frac{2\pi^2\,Me^4}{ch^3}$$

Bohr rewrote his equation in the form

$$\nu = \frac{Rc}{m^2} - \frac{Rc}{n^2}$$

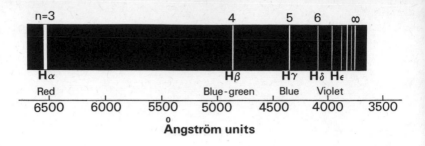

n=3　　　　　　　4　　　　5　6　　∞

Hα　　　　　　　Hβ　　　Hγ　Hδ Hε

Red　　　　　Blue-green　Blue　Violet

6500　　6000　　5500　　5000　　4500　　4000　　3500

Ångström units

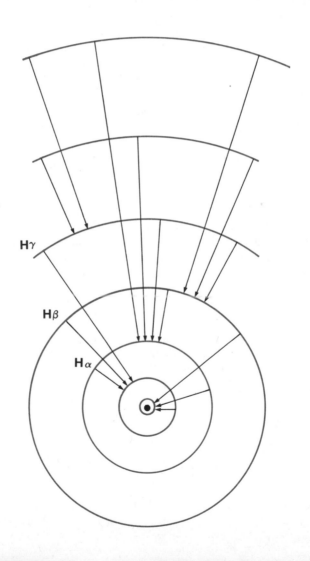

Hγ

Hβ

Hα

20 The levels of energy of the hydrogen atom according to
the theory of Bohr. The arrows represent the quantic transitions
of an electron from an orbit of higher energy to one of lower energy.
The excess energy is emitted as light of wavelength
characteristic of the change of energy. The three transitions,
H α, H β and H γ, which lead to the second level of energy,
correspond to the lines of the Balmer's series shown at the top –
the only series in the visible spectrum.

in perfect analogy with Balmer's formula. The only requirement is
that the constant **R** must be the same in both cases. If so, then a
simple calculation using the known values of **e, M, c, h** and π
shows that the theoretical expression agrees with Rydberg's constant to within $0 \cdot 1 \%$. The *Bohr atom* was fully verified.

Bohr achieved his success through a complete disregard for
classical physics, and this same disregard allowed him to bypass the
problem of the atom's stability. Admittedly, the equations of
electromagnetism required that an electric charge moving in a
closed orbit should radiate light, but there seemed no reason to
assume that this should present any difficulties because it had
already been assumed that light is emitted as a result of a quantum
jump from one orbit to another. According to Bohr, an electron
would not radiate while moving in its quantum orbit. This was
plausible enough, since it also explained why atoms were so stable.

In a way, Bohr's theory had something of the nature of a
fascinating hybrid monster. It showed atoms to be miniature Solar
Systems, with their electrons moving round their nuclei according
to the rules of Newtonian mechanics, and yet out of all the movements possible in classical theory, only a very small number were
acceptable in quantum theory. In contrast to classical laws, the
emission or absorption of light cannot take place for electrons in

21 Niels Bohr (1885–1962) developed the first successful
theory of atomic structure, and he and his students have been at
the centre of the development of quantum ideas.

quantum orbits except for photons of energy $h\nu$, which would result
in a quantum jump from one quantum orbit of energy E_m to
another of energy E_n, changing the energy of the electron by a
quantity

$$E_m - E_n = h\nu$$

Despite its hybrid nature, the theory proved to be very useful and
admirably precise. During the decade following the publication of
Bohr's fundamental paper, the theory was considerably extended
and perfected. It would be difficult to give a full account of all the
developments, but something must at least be said here about the
most important and relevant points.

First, the theorists began to try to interpret the spectra of atoms
more complex than that of hydrogen. These calculations involved
various approximations, and the final precision was bound to
suffer, but on the whole the theory was found to be satisfactory,
and physicists started to unravel the complexities of the spectral
lines.

This systematic research into atomic structure soon explained
the surprising regularities of Mendeleyev's table. It was quickly
realised that the atomic number given to each element corresponded to the number of electrons moving round the central
nucleus of the atom, but to explain the periodicity of the table it
was necessary to apply various empirical rules, and in particular,
it was assumed that although several electrons can co-exist in the
same orbit, their number must be limited. In fact any orbit can
become saturated with electrons, after which it can accept no more.

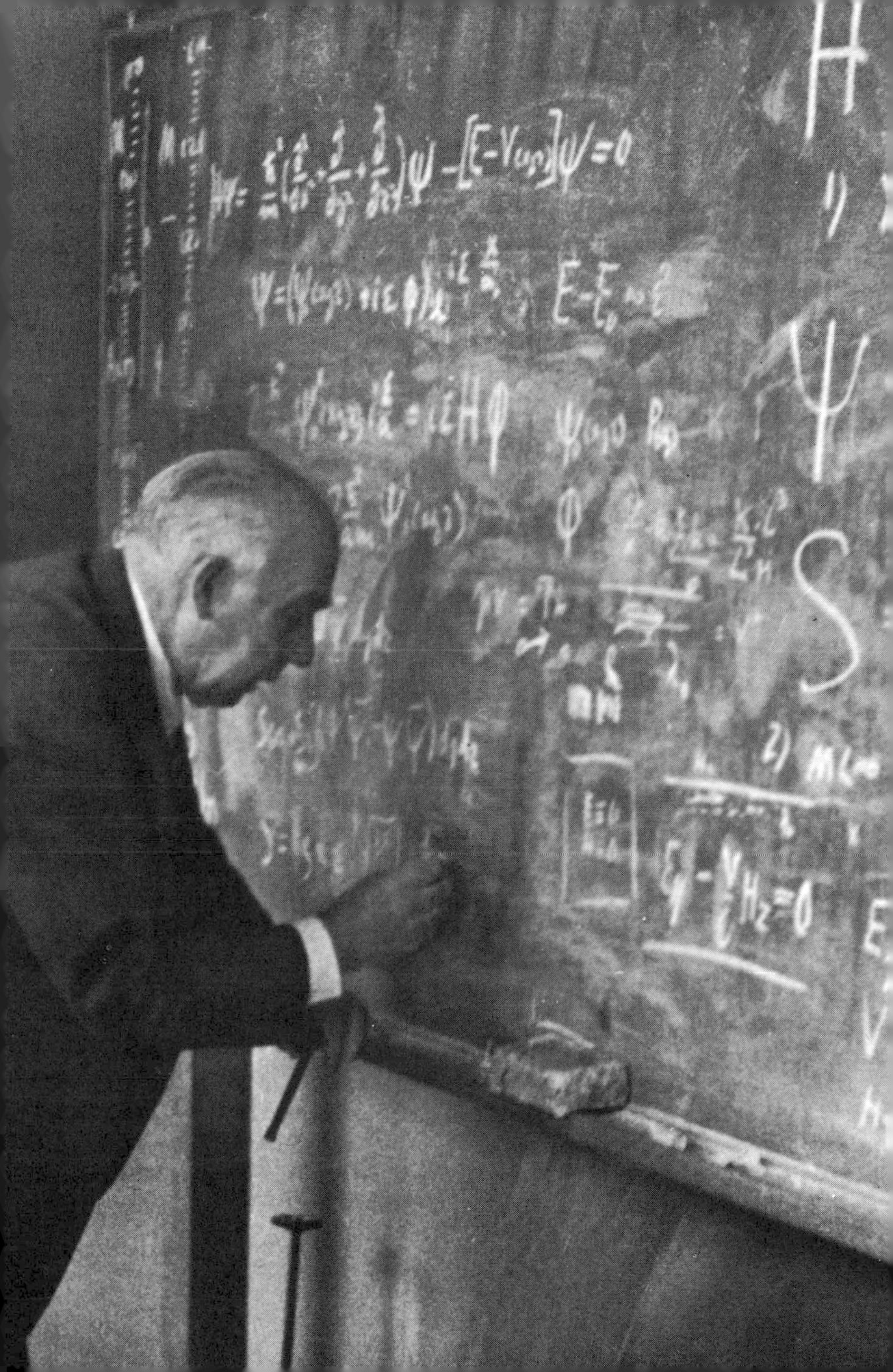

22 The lightest atom is that of hydrogen, with a single
positively charged proton and an orbiting electron.
The atom is electrically neutral. As the proton
is nearly two thousand times heavier than the electron,
the mass of the atom is concentrated in the nucleus.
The radius of the nucleus is about 10^{-13} cm compared to
10^{-8} cm for the complete hydrogen atom. The atom is
therefore mainly empty space. The next heaviest atom is
an isotope of hydrogen – deuterium or heavy hydrogen – which
chemically is identical to hydrogen since there is just one
orbiting electron. The nucleus is, however, twice as heavy,
having in addition to the proton a single uncharged neutron
of about the same mass as the proton, Carbon comprises
six protons (atomic number = 6) and six neutrons, giving an
atomic weight of 12; there are six surrounding electrons
to keep the atom neutral. In the Bohr theory the electrons can
exist only in a discrete set of orbits, or quantum states.

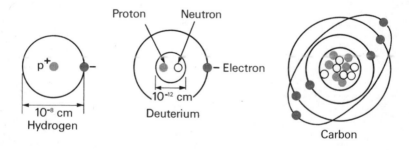

10⁻⁸ cm
Hydrogen

Proton   Neutron

– Electron
10^{-12} cm
Deuterium

Carbon

The first (inner) orbit can contain only two electrons, the second orbit can hold up to eight, the third orbit up to eighteen, and so on. By accepting these numbers, together with the assumption that electrons can occupy new orbits only if all the inner orbits are saturated, it finally becomes possible to give a logical interpretation of the periodic table of elements.

Meanwhile, the hydrogen atom remained a source of endless problems even though it had to be regarded as the simplest of all cases. It was found that the spectral lines that Bohr had calculated so exactly were, in many cases, made up of several component lines very close together, so that they had what became known as *fine structure*. The importance of this structure was stressed by Arnold Sommerfeld, whose theoretical contributions to the theory of atomic structure were so great that the Bohr atom is often referred to as the Bohr-Sommerfeld atom. His treatise *Atombau und Spektrallinien* remained the standard work for many years.

Bohr's original rule applied only to very simple movements, such as circular motion. Actually, an electron moving round a nucleus, or a planet moving round the sun, will generally travel not in a circle, but in an ellipse. Sommerfeld's first contribution was to extend the theory to quantise all types of motion, and in so doing, he used Bohr's mathematical framework to construct a powerful and flexible theory.

One of Sommerfeld's immensely important achievements was to link quantum theory with relativity. If we calculate the speed of an electron moving round a nucleus in a circular or elliptical orbit, we arrive at a value of the order of 1,000 km/sec. This is very small compared with the velocity of light, but it is still large enough to justify the use of relativistic mechanics in order to fit the observational data. Sommerfeld solved this mathematical problem brilliantly, and was able to work out the fine structure of the hydrogen spectrum – a result which is rightly regarded as a triumph both for relativity and for quantum theory.

However, all these successes had nothing directly to do with the frequency of the lines, and there was no theory to explain their intensity. It was not only that the lines were of unequal intensity; there were some lines which were never seen at all, so that they had to be assigned a zero intensity. And yet how could this be justified? Paradoxically, it would have been much easier to explain on the basis of the old Maxwell-Lorentz electromagnetic theory, from which the intensity of a line can be calulated as soon as its frequency is known. Unfortunately, the link between atomic theory and classical electromagnetism had been definitely severed.

Once again it was Bohr who saw that there might still be a connection between the two theories. He knew that quantum physics and classical physics differ in one vital respect. With the former, energy can be changed only in discrete amounts, while with the latter there can be continuous variation. If the quantum jump has a very small value, the result will be an outward aspect of continuity, and this makes it possible to see how, in certain cases, classical and quantum laws can be combined.

One such case applies to a planetary electron which is very energetic, and which moves in an orbit of large radius, since if it falls toward the nucleus in small jumps, losing only a very small fraction of its total energy with each jump, it will give the impression of continuous fall and will appear to follow the laws of Newtonian mechanics. Consequently, it is logical to assume that the light emitted during this nearly continuous fall will be much the same as predicted by classical electromagnetism. In this case, then, we know how to calculate both the frequencies and the intensities of the light emitted by the atom.

Such were the methods by which Bohr tried to associate quantum physics with classical physics. By ingenious adaptations of classical formulae, he was able to work out the intensities of all the spectral lines. And in spite of its ambiguities, this *principle of correspondence* proved to be extremely useful, particularly when it was perfected in later years. By then, however, attention had been directed to a new subject – the new quantum mechanics – and it is to quantum mechanics that we must now turn.

3 The equations know best

3 The equations know best

Two heads on one body

With the Bohr atom, the law of quanta was definitely accepted. It accounted for so many of the phenomena inexplicable by classical physics that scientists as a whole resigned themselves to accepting the 'uninvited guest' that Planck had introduced. It was a matter of giving way to its demands and learning to make use of its power.

And yet during the first twenty years of the present century, progress was painfully slow. Bohr's theory had given a brilliant interpretation of the spectrum of the simplest atom, hydrogen, but it became much less clear when applied to more complex atoms, or to molecules. Various *ad hoc* hypotheses had to be tacked on to the general principles, and as the theory was extended it became more and more complicated.

One of these difficulties was particularly significant and inherent in the basic concept. Although the ideas of quantum theory were so revolutionary, they were made up of nothing more than a mixture of recipes which allowed the introduction of the discontinuity principle into the language of classical physics. If Planck's constant were to be given its proper place, the whole of mechanics would have to be reconstructed.

Then came the second quantum revolution. It was started almost simultaneously by two young scientists whose outlooks were very different and who knew nothing about each other's work. One was a lone worker, strongly influenced by the work of Einstein and Poincaré, whole bold and subtle mind was concerned with the analysis of the great theories of optics and mechanics. The other was a brilliant mathematical physicist who had been inspired by the ideas of Bohr, and who lived in the lively atmosphere of a university where quantum theory was very much in the public eye.

Though their objectives were the same, their methods of approach and the concept which guided them had almost nothing in common.

Louis de Broglie discovered that the secret of quanta lay in a general law of nature, the dual character of waves and particles. Just as light is not purely a wave, neither is a piece of matter purely a particle; instead the universe is made up of entities which are waves and particles at the same time. He showed that the properties of these 'matter waves' were hidden behind the quantum laws of Planck and Bohr, and he set out to discover just what they might be. Shortly afterwards Erwin Schrödinger, on the same basis, produced the famous equation which led on to the development of *wave mechanics*.

At the same time, Werner Heisenberg achieved a parallel result. Instead of trying to understand the origin of quantum states, he simply accepted them, and worked out a remarkable method of calculation which allowed him to study them without involving the détours and uncertainties of Bohr's theory. This was the *matrix mechanics*, which he perfected together with Born and Jordan, and which Dirac used with considerable success.

Physics now found itself equipped with two new sections of mechanics. They were totally different in their methods and their approach, but their application led to the same results. Schrödinger soon demonstrated the mathematical equivalence of the two theories, and a single mechanics resulted, known today as quantum mechanics. Although its methods were borrowed mainly from wave mechanics, its language was more nearly that of the theory of matrices, so that it kept the skeleton of the first theory and the philosophy of the second. More will be said about this important problem later, but meanwhile let us describe this new physics and what it managed to achieve.

Since quantum mechanics has been able to predict a vast number of phenomena with a precision even greater than that of the legendary accuracy of astronomy, it must certainly be regarded as one of the greatest branches of science. Even more remarkable, perhaps, is the fact that equations of such significance can have been deduced from reasoning which is so abstract and so general. Heinrich Hertz once wrote about Maxwell's equations, 'One cannot help feeling that these mathematical formulae have an independent existence and a true intelligence. They know more than we do and more than those who discovered them; they will give out more information than has ever been put into them.'

Matter-waves

For a long time the science of optics hesitated between Newton's corpuscular hypothesis and Huygens' wave theory. The corpuscular idea was generally accepted until the beginning of the nineteenth century, after which it was more or less abandoned and the wave theory replaced it. Then, quite suddenly, Einstein showed that the two theories were not mutually exclusive, but that each had a great deal to be said for it, and each had its own role in science. To make the situation even more complex, a curious relationship existed between them, because the properties of the waves controlled those of the photons.

This rather perplexed hesitation was entirely unknown in mechanics. After all, a particle of matter is a particle of matter, and nobody had foreseen any difficulties on this score. The theory of quanta came from quite other sources, and the main problem was to understand the restrictions which it placed on classical movements, together with its emphasis on the significance of whole numbers. The fact that the same constant **h** occurred in both optics and mechanics indicated that there might be a connecting link between the two, but in all honesty the link was a very fragile one.

After a long study of the structure of the great physical theories, and worried about the problem of quanta, de Broglie came to the conclusion that the difficulties facing optics and mechanics were not so fundamentally different as might be thought. During 1923 he suddenly realised, with a flash of intuition, that the dual nature of light as discovered by Einstein – part-wave, part-particle – must be due to a general law of nature which affected all material particles, notably electrons. He then had the remarkable idea that in spite of appearances, matter itself might possess wave-like properties which were responsible for the strange behaviour of atoms.

In this book it is not possible to describe the mathematical analogies which played such a large part in de Broglie's researches, but some attempt can at least be made to show how he reached the conclusions that he did. First, a simple experiment will show how the whole numbers, so puzzling in Bohr's theory, can occur quite naturally in a wave phenomenon.

Take one of the ends of a long rope and shake it roughly. The waves will start close to your hand, and will spread along to the far end of the rope. If the far end is tied to a tree, the waves will be reflected, and there will be interference between the waves which are moving in opposite directions.

The resulting movement will be generally chaotic, and the waves have a tendency to cancel each other out. Now continue to shake the rope, but gradually increase or decrease the tension upon it. Suddenly, the movement will become orderly and will start to follow a stable pattern. At that stage, only a very small effort is needed to sustain the motion, and it will even seem that your hand is following the motion of the rope.

The propagation of the waves cannot now be distinguished, and the rope seems to oscillate regularly up and down over the same

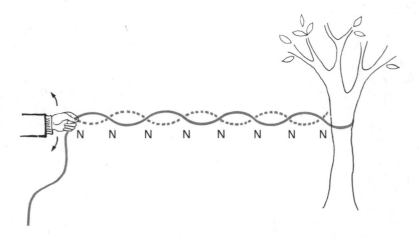

23 A stationary wave on a rope. The points **N** are the nodes of the vibration.

points. It has been separated into a number of arcs of equal length, and all the points on any particular arc are moving up or down at the same time. Adjacent arcs are in opposite phase, one moving down while the other comes up, while the point joining two adjacent arcs (the *node* of vibration) remains motionless. Obviously, the end of the rope which is fixed to the tree marks one node, while there is another node close to your hand. The overall phenomenon is that of what is called a *stationary wave*.

One important conclusion can be drawn from all this. A stationary wave is a stable motion characterised by the separation of the rope into a number of oscillating arcs, separated by motionless nodes. The number of arcs is not fixed, and a different tension, or a different degree of shaking, would produce a different number. But, and this is the vital point, there will always be a *whole number* of arcs. By definition, the length of the stationary wave is equal to twice the length of an individual arc, so that the wavelength is highly significant. If we change from one stationary wave to another, the wavelength cannot change in a continuous manner, but changing the number of arcs will mean that the wavelength will be altered from one value to another.

Now, if a wave is turned back on itself by some obstacle or other, only the stationary waves will remain stable and will not extend. This happens with the sound-waves in an organ tube, radio waves in an aerial, or stationary light-waves between two mirrors.

This latter example is particularly significant. Einstein showed that any light-wave is associated with 'particles of light' whose energy is determined by the frequency of the wave. We have just noted that if this wave is stationary, then its wavelength (and consequently its frequency) must be defined in terms of whole numbers. It follows that these same numbers must also control the energy of the photons, which is another way of saying that their energy will be quantised.

We are now in a position to understand the bold reasoning which led de Broglie to his theory of wave mechanics. Bohr's theory, he noted, associated whole numbers with particles of matter, and this is how it distinguished between movements which were 'stable' and those which were not. Could this be an indication of the existence of some unknown 'wave of matter', which would be to the particle of matter what the 'light-wave' is to the photon? For instance, it might be that this wave could exist only in an atom which was in a stationary condition. If so, then the stable movements of the electron would be governed by whole numbers taken direct from wave theory, and these, after all, were the same as the whole numbers introduced by Bohr's theory.

De Broglie realised that his situation was the exact reverse of that of Einstein twenty years earlier. Einstein had known about the theory of light-waves, and had wanted to create a corpuscular theory; knowing the frequency v of the wave, and wanting to define the energy E of the photon, he had hit on the idea of using Planck's formula $E = hv$. De Broglie, on the other hand, knew nothing definite about the wave of matter which he had just postulated, and had to work out its properties by using the properties of particles of matter, where he had mechanics to guide him. He then assumed that the energy of a particle must always be linked with the frequency of its wave by the formula $E = hv$, which gave a relationship between the energy of the photon and the frequency of the light-wave. He knew that his formula must be the reverse of Einstein's, because he knew the amount of energy but was completely ignorant about the frequency of the wave.

He borrowed the value of this energy from relativity theory, according to which the total energy of any piece of matter is equal to the product of its mass and the square of the velocity of light (the famous equation $E = mc^2$). Combining this with Planck's formula, de Broglie proposed that any particle of matter of mass m is associated with a wave whose frequency is given by the equation

$$h v = mc^2$$

From this equation, he next tried to work out the wavelength λ of the matter-wave, and again he had recourse to relativity theory, though the exact procedure is too difficult to describe here. He found that the wavelength can be expressed by a formula now known as de Broglie's equation:

$$\lambda = \frac{h}{mv}$$

which, by means of the mass and velocity of a corpuscle (both of which are expressed in purely mechanical terms), gives the fundamental parameter characterising the matter-wave.

By means of this remarkable formula, de Broglie was able to determine the wavelength associated with an electron in a planetary atom. Since an atom is a stable system, he naturally supposed that the only possible orbits for an electron are those which correspond to a stationary wave of matter, and which contain a whole number of wavelengths. He looked for orbits which satisfied these conditions, and came back exactly to the predictions drawn from Bohr's theory.

The success of this calculation marked the beginning of a new science, *wave mechanics*. By replacing Bohr's formal laws with the properties of matter-waves, de Broglie was able to combine quantum theory with general wave theory, and thereby to link optics with mechanics, admittedly in a rather unexpected fashion. And yet this new conception of the physical world naturally raised a host of fresh problems. Thus, in de Broglie's reasoning it is not specified that a particle is regarded as an electron at any particular moment, except that the numerical value of the mass adopted for the calculation corresponds to that of an electron. If de Broglie's view were correct, it would follow that there would be a wave associated with any particle or object, whether it be an atom, a molecule or anything else, and whatever might be its mass or volume. The next question was to find out why these waves had never been detected. This was of vital importance, and involved the application of the new mechanics.

For instance, let us take the example of a vehicle weighing 2,000 kg moving at a speed of 100 km/h, and try to work out the wavelength of the corresponding wave of matter. De Broglie's formula gives the value

$$\lambda = \frac{1}{1,000,000,000,000,000,000,000,000,000,000,000} \text{ cm}$$

To make this number rather more intelligible, it may be said that the wavelength is thirty million million times smaller than the diameter of an electron. Therefore, it may be argued that this very smallness means that it is impossible to detect the wavelength of a wave of matter associated with a vehicle or any other microscopic object.

To clear this question up, we must turn to geometrical optics. Everyone knows that this deals with the paths of light-rays in vacuum or in transparent media, and we all remember, from our schooldays, how these rays change in direction when they pass through a prism or a lens, or when they are reflected by a mirror. The nature of a light-wave is not concerned in this theory, and we are in effect studying how light would behave if it were made up of a shower of particles moving along definite paths. It is a sort of mechanics of light-particles, and the fact that we have conveniently forgotten about waves does not prevent the theory from explaining a great many phenomena. Indeed, it means that we can work out all the essential principles of optical instruments.

So far, however, we have been discussing wave optics, and there are definite limitations to this way of reasoning. We can ignore the wave nature of light only if the paths of the 'particles of light' are not too curved. If some sort of obstacle, for example a marked inhomogeneity in the transport medium, or simply the end of the screen, deflects the light so that the radius of curvature of the path becomes as small as the wavelength, the laws of geometrical optics break down, and the wave concept becomes of supreme importance. Geometrical optics is valid only if the radius of curvature of the path is much greater than the wavelength.

24 Louis de Broglie (born 1892) suggested in 1923 that electrons sometimes exhibit the properties of waves with wavelengths inversely proportional to their momenta. This concept was confirmed soon after by experiment and heralded the beginning of the wave-theory of matter.

Next, suppose that the vehicle in our previous example starts to turn in a circle of 10 metres radius. The wavelength given by de Broglie's formula will now fit into the radius of this circle 10^{39} times. If we had taken the case of a 'microscopic' particle, weighing a thousand-millionth of a milligramme and turning in a circle with a radius of one micron, and at the same speed, the radius of curvature of the path would still be a hundred million million times greater than the wavelength.

Let us agree, with de Broglie, that there is a close analogy between light and matter, between optics and mechanics, and between waves of matter and waves of light. It is at once clear that the motion of our vehicle, or any other 'macroscopic' object, comes into the range of the geometrical optics of matter-waves. Therefore, the effects of those matter-waves can never be detected.

But what exactly is meant by 'the geometrical optics of matter-waves'? Just as true geometrical optics involves the study of the movements of light-particles along light-rays, so we must consider the movement of particles of matter along 'matter-rays'; that is to say, the movement of material bodies along definite paths. Yet we already know about this sort of science: it is nothing more nor less than classical mechanics. Classical mechanics is the optical geometry of matter-waves, and, because of the smallness of the wavelength for macroscopic bodies, this mechanical 'geometry' will always be valid on our scale.

On the other hand, if for a certain body in a certain state of motion the wavelength calculated according to de Broglie is large enough, and if the paths are sufficiently curved, then classical mechanics will no longer be able to give a correct description of the phenomena. Everything will take place on the atomic scale, mainly because the masses of the electrons and other fundamental particles are so small. This, of course, explains why classical mechanics fails in this sort of example, and it also explains the success of the calculations of the Bohr orbits as worked out by wave mechanics.

Not long afterwards, the existence of matter-waves was proved in a more direct manner. This was achieved by considering electrons which, up to then, had been regarded as small marbles, and repeating all the classical experiments of wave optics. The phenomena of interference and diffraction, well known in optics and described by the wave theory, were obtained by substituting electrons for light. The measured wavelengths agreed perfectly with those calculated from de Broglie's formula, and this was obviously a brilliant justification of the theory.

Although this investigation solidly established the analogy between the fundamental properties of matter and light, it is undeniable that in some ways the electron remains more 'wavelike' than the photon. The electron is much more inclined to obey the laws of classical mechanics than light is likely to follow the laws of geometrical optics. This is because the wavelengths of the electrons usually produced in the laboratory are much shorter than those of visible light, and are indeed more comparable with the wavelengths of x-rays.

This fact has an important application in the *electron microscope*, which can give a magnification tens of times greater than that of the best optical microscope. Its importance in many fields of science and technology is enormous, and so far as microbiology is concerned it is quite invaluable.

What has been said in the last few pages should provide a clue to the workings of the electron microscope. If light strictly obeyed the laws of geometrical optics, it would be possible to construct optical microscopes which would be as powerful as anyone could wish, given the necessary practical techniques, of course. Unfortunately, however, this is not the case. Because of the diffraction of light, the image of a point source is not itself a point, but a small patch whose dimensions are of the same order as the wavelength of the light being used. If two points of light being studied are sufficiently close together, their image will overlap, and it will be impossible to distinguish one from the other, so that there is no chance of observing an object which is smaller than the wavelength of the light concerned. There is no escape from this limitation, because it stems not from any defect in the construction of the microscope but from the nature of light itself. In other words, there is an absolute limit to the power of an optical microscope.

The only way to overcome this limit is to use, within the microscope, light whose wavelength is shorter than that of visible light, so that the diffraction will be reduced. The image of a point in the microscope will still be a patch, but it will be a smaller patch, and the ideal conditions of geometrical optics will be more nearly satisfied. Microscopes using ultra-violet rays have been made with success, but even shorter wavelengths are needed. X-rays, of course, have extremely short wavelengths, but we do not know how to construct a lens that will operate with x-rays; and without lenses, one cannot have a microscope.

This is where wave mechanics comes in. We know that the wavelength of the electrons available to us are shorter than those of x-rays, which means that the images would be of very good quality; and even though it is not at present possible to make a lens that will operate with x-rays, we do know how to make a lens which will work with electrons. Since electrons are in effect small electric charges, we can deflect them along any required 'optical ray' by passing them through suitable electrical and magnetic fields. In this way we can produce a microscope of great power, simply because the wavelengths of the waves of matter are so short.

But when de Broglie presented his Ph.D. thesis in 1924, these successes lay in the future. Einstein was one of the few physicists to understand the importance of the work, and it was mainly due to him that the ideas of wave mechanics spread quickly through the large German-speaking universities.

At this time the Austrian physicist Erwin Schrödinger was a professor at the University of Zürich. His researches into the statistical equilibrium of gases and into radiations were closely linked with Einstein's work. When Schrödinger first became aware of de Broglie's thesis, in 1926, he made the very wise decision to follow up one of the important clues of the theory – the analogy between the mathematical schemes of classical mechanics and of geometrical optics. To simplify his calculations he abandoned relativity, which had given so great an initial impetus, and tried to find an equation which would define the motions of matter-waves.

He duly found it. Over a period of one year he produced seven lengthy fundamental papers which contained nearly all the mathematical apparatus of wave mechanics, and his calculations have hardly been modified to this day. In his first paper he gave the famous equation which bears his name, and he solved it for several important cases:

$$\frac{\partial^2 \psi}{\partial x^2} + \frac{\partial^2 \psi}{\partial y^2} + \frac{\partial^2 \psi}{\partial z^2} - \frac{8\pi^2 m}{h^2} V(x, y, z, t) \psi = \frac{4\pi i m}{h} \frac{\partial \psi}{\partial t}$$

If we take Schrödinger's calculations literally, the general impres-

25 Erwin Schrödinger (1887–1961). His great contribution was to formulate mathematically the theory of wave mechanics.

sion is decidedly strange, because an atom is regarded as a sort of vibrating membrane which extends to infinity and whose vibrations are in rhythm with Bohr's frequencies. While de Broglie had considered that the particle existed within the wave, Schrödinger did away with the particle altogether. His theory did not deal with particles of matter: his universe contained waves, and waves only.

By means of difficult calculations founded on simple mathematical principles, Schrödinger deduced from his equation all the results of Bohr and de Broglie with regard to the hydrogen atom, and in a more general way, all the known results of quantum

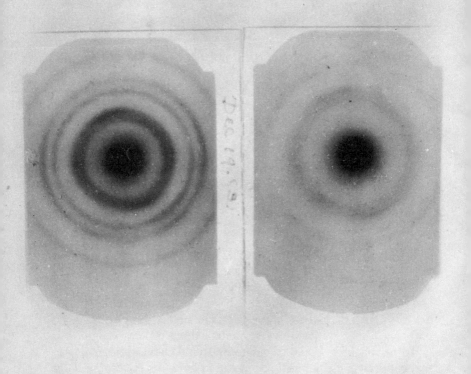

SPARK GAP **20·7** mms   10·7 mms

26 Two of the earliest electron diffraction photographs (1927), which demonstrated the wave nature of electrons and confirmed de Broglie's 'electron wave' hypothesis.

theory. Without introducing any supplementary hypotheses, he also accounted for almost all the corrections that had been gradually tacked on to the old theory to make it agree with the observed facts. Then he realised that his conclusions were in perfect accord with those of another theory which had just been published, and which must now be described.

A × B and B × A

Werner Heisenberg had studied under Sommerfeld. He was not quite twenty-two when, in 1923, he became assistant to Max Born at the famous German university of Göttingen. This was the same year in which, from Paris, de Broglie published his first paper on what was to become wave mechanics, and made the first mention of matter-waves.

The viewpoints of de Broglie and Max Born were completely different. Born made no attempt to explain quanta; he was quite ready to accept them as they were, and his problem was to find the best ways of using them. According to him, the difficulties facing physicists stemmed from their concepts of time, space, position and velocity, which were borrowed from classical physics. On the atomic scale, there were no rules to measure the lengths and no clocks to define the periods, and there seemed little sense in discussing things which could not be measured.

In 1925, Heisenberg tried to portray this radical philosophy by means of a remarkable calculation. He asked himself a series of questions, and did his best to answer them. First, what can we observe of an atom? – the light that it emits. What do we know about this light? – its frequency and its intensity. Now, quantum theory teaches that this light is emitted during the transition of the atom from one quantum state to another. More precisely, when an electron passes from a state of energy E_i to a different state of energy E_k, it will emit a photon whose frequency ν_{ik} is given by the equation

$$\nu_{ik} = \frac{E_i}{h} - \frac{E_k}{h}$$

Now, if the frequency is ν_{ik}, what will be the intensity of the radiation? According to Einstein's theory of light, the intensity will be determined by the relevant number of photons of frequency ν_{ik}. And since each of these photons is emitted by an atom during its quantum transition between states **i** and **k,** the corresponding intensity will be greater when the chances of this transition are more probable.

Heisenberg concluded that if we can calculate the series of values E_1, E_2, E_3 ... which refer to the energy of the atom and to the transition probability from one of these values to another, then we shall know all about the light which must be emitted by the atom. He added that since no individual parameter is measurable, no satisfactory theory can initially contain any other concept.

Let us note here that the frequencies of the emitted light, together with the transition probabilities, have to be identified by a symbol with two indices, one representing the original state of the atom and the other representing the final state. For instance, the probability of changing from state 7 to state 2 can be written as **P (7, 2)**. Heisenberg then had the idea of representing the energy not by a single number, but by a matrix of numbers, as follows:

$$
a = \begin{bmatrix}
a_{11} & a_{12} & a_{13} & \cdot & \cdot & \cdot & a_{1n} & \cdot & \cdot & \cdot \\
a_{21} & a_{22} & a_{23} & \cdot & \cdot & \cdot & a_{2n} & \cdot & \cdot & \cdot \\
a_{31} & a_{32} & a_{33} & \cdot & \cdot & \cdot & a_{3n} & \cdot & \cdot & \cdot \\
\cdot & \cdot & \cdot & \cdot & \cdot & \cdot & \cdot & & & \\
\cdot & \cdot & \cdot & \cdot & \cdot & \cdot & \cdot & & & \\
\cdot & \cdot & \cdot & \cdot & \cdot & \cdot & \cdot & & & \\
a_{n1} & a_{n2} & a_{n3} & \cdot & \cdot & \cdot & a_{nn} & \cdot & \cdot & \cdot \\
\cdot & \cdot & \cdot & \cdot & \cdot & \cdot & \cdot & & &
\end{bmatrix}
$$

This matrix may be said to have the form of an 'infinite square'. Each element (for example, a_{ik}) must be related, in some way or other, to the transition between the state numbered i and the state numbered k. But in order to calculate the frequencies and the luminous energies, Heisenberg had to build up an 'atomic mechanics', introducing other parameters besides energy. For example, we must bring in the positions and the velocities of the particles. Admittedly, these cannot be directly observed in the atom, but they certainly cannot be ignored completely, at least in the intermediate stages of the calculation. Since these parameters could be used in calculating the energy matrices, Heisenberg came to the conclusion that all the physical properties could also be described in terms of matrices, which would correspond to the energy matrices.

In order to write down the relations between these parameters, the first step was to find out how to use these matrices. He began with addition, and found that if **a** and **b** are two tables representing two physical parameters, then their sum **a** + **b** can be given quite simply in the form:

$$
a+b = \begin{bmatrix}
a_{11}+b_{11} & a_{12}+b_{12} & a_{13}+b_{13} & \ldots & a_{1n}+b_{1n} & \ldots \\
a_{21}+b_{21} & a_{22}+b_{22} & a_{23}+b_{23} & \ldots & a_{2n}+b_{2n} & \ldots \\
a_{31}+b_{31} & a_{32}+b_{32} & a_{33}+b_{33} & \ldots & a_{3n}+b_{3n} & \ldots \\
\cdot & \cdot & \cdot & \cdots & \cdot & \\
\cdot & \cdot & \cdot & \cdots & \cdot & \\
\cdot & \cdot & \cdot & \cdots & \cdot & \\
a_{n1}+b_{n1} & a_{n2}+b_{n2} & a_{n3}+b_{n3} & & a_{nn}+b_{nn} & \ldots \\
\cdot & \cdot & \cdot & & \cdot & \\
\cdot & \cdot & \cdot & & \cdot & \\
\cdot & \cdot & \cdot & & \cdot &
\end{bmatrix}
$$

By applying this rule, it is easy to see that the sum of **b** + **a** will be given by the same table as for **a** + **b**. However, the situation was markedly complicated when Heisenberg went on to define the product of two parameters, **ab**. He showed that in the corresponding table, the number at the intersection of the **i-th** line and the **k-th** column can be written as:

$$(ab)_{ik} = a_{i1}b_{1k} + a_{i2}b_{2k} + a_{i3}b_{3k} + \ldots + a_{in}b_{nk} + \ldots$$

Again using the same rule, it is clear that the matrix representing the product of **a** × **b** is not the same as that which corresponds to the product of **b** × **a**. We find:

$$(ba)_{ik} = b_{i1}a_{1k} + b_{i2}a_{2k} + b_{i3}a_{3k} + \ldots + b_{in}a_{nk} + \ldots$$

and, in general, this number is not equal to the first one. This result can be expressed symbolically by

$$ab \neq ba$$

and we say that the matrix multiplication is *non-commutative*.

Heisenberg used this curious property to introduce the indispensable Planck's constant into his theory. He showed that if a particle of mass **m** moves through a distance **x** in a specified direction with velocity **v**, and if the matrices associated with these parameters are represented by the same letters **x** and **v**, we arrive at the equation

$$xv - vx = \frac{h}{2\pi i m}$$

where **h** is Planck's constant and **i** is the 'imaginary' unit $\sqrt{-1}$. Later, he used this equality to draw up his famous uncertainty relations.

Note, however, that since Planck's constant is so extremely small, the factor **h/m** will be appreciable only when the particle under consideration is of very low mass. For solid bodies on our scale this factor is negligible, and we can write simply

$$xv - vx = 0$$

as if we were dealing with ordinary numbers. In other words, the unfamiliar rules in Heisenberg's calculations apply only to the world of atoms, where the particles are of sufficiently small mass.

At this stage, there is every excuse for wondering how considerations which are so abstract, not to say vague, can ever lead to a physical theory. It is not sufficient to say that the numbers which appear in the matrices (particularly those corresponding to energy) are related to the frequencies and intensities of the emitted light; we must look for something more concrete. This is what Heisenberg did, very skilfully, by using Bohr's correspondence principle.

There still remained the greatest difficulty of all: that of calculating the actual numbers. Since Heisenberg had now found how to add and multiply his matrices, he had provided himself with what might be called an *algebra*, and so he could deal with each matrix as though it were a single number of a particular kind. With these new 'numbers', he could in effect make any calculations that he liked, and in particular he could adapt the matrices, which represented physical parameters, to satisfy equations. And yet – what equations? Heisenberg had the surprising idea of using the equations of classical mechanics, with the important difference that the ordinary numbers were replaced by infinite matrices.

He could now put his theory to the test, and see whether it worked or not. First, he proved that his equations obeyed Bohr's frequency laws, and that they were satisfied only by certain particular values of energy. This brought him back to the existence of the quantum states of an atom, and as a test he chose the comparatively simple yet precise case of the light emitted by a molecule in a state of vibration. This calculation not only gave him the same result as that of Bohr's theory, but also contained the correction factor which had had to be introduced to reconcile the theory with experimental results.

Once he had established the success of his calculations, Heisenberg gained many followers. Of these the most celebrated were Max Born and Pascual Jordan, with whom he had collaborated from the outset, and Dirac, who had been working at Cambridge, and at about the same time had produced an analogous theory which was even more abstract. It was Dirac who had made the famous remark: 'Quantum mechanics is simple; it is simply classical mechanics using a non-commutative algebra.'

The tables used by Heisenberg were already well-known to mathematicians under the name of *matrices*, and for this reason the theory was called *matrix mechanics*. With the help of mathematical techniques, this new branch of science made rapid progress. It became very precise, and its predictions were found to agree with experimental results without the need to introduce any supplementary hypotheses. It was born out of abstract concepts, but it replaced Bohr's rather intuitive theory because it had a sounder structure and its results were more accurate.

By now the wave mechanics of de Broglie and Schrödinger, founded on totally different physical concepts and methods of calculations, were being found to give almost the same results. Theorists do not like coincidences, particularly when they are of great importance, and there was every reason for finding an explanation. Actually this was done in the same year, when Schrödinger discovered the basic equation of wave mechanics. To make his reasoning clear, we must introduce a new and important concept, that of the *operator*.

An operator is the symbolical representation of any relationship between an object in one set and another object which may be in the same set or in any other set. This is a very general concept, but the very complicated operators so often used by mathematicians in abstract entities can be illustrated by means of simple examples drawn from everyday experience. When we interchange two books on a shelf, we are applying the *permutation operator;* when a removal man makes a heavy crate slide, he is applying the *translation operator;* if he moves the crate by pushing it over on to its edge, he is applying the *rotation operator*. Many instructive examples of this sort could be given, but for the moment it will be sufficient to concentrate upon the permutation of the books.

27 The problem of the arrangement of books on a shelf.

Let us say that **A, B** and **C** are three books which occupy positions **1, 2** and **3** on the shelf (figure 27 (**a**)). Consider two permutation operators. The first, which will be designated by (**1;2**) will make the interchange between the books which occupy positions **1** and **2**, while the other (**1;3**) will interchange the books between positions **1** and **3**. If we apply operator (**1;2**) to (**a**), we obtain the arrangement in (**b**). If we apply operator (**1;3**) we obtain (**c**). Now apply operator (**1;3**) to (**b**). The new order will be as in (**d**), which is the result of applying first operator (**1;2**) and then operator (**1;3**) to the original (**a**). By definition we can say that we have applied the *product* of operators (**1;2**) and (**1;3**). This can be written as:

$$(1;3)\ (1;2)$$

This gives us a new permutation operator, which when applied to (**a**) will lead directly to (**d**). We could just as well have applied operator (**1;3**) to (**b**). This would be equivalent to applying operator (**1;2**) to (**c**) and will give (**e**). This represents the arrangement resulting from the successive applications of operators (**1;3**) and (**1;2**) to the original (**a**). In other words, we have applied the *product* of operators (**1;3**) and (**1;2**), which may be written as:

$$(1;2)\ (1;3)$$

and is a new operator leading directly to (**e**) from the old (**a**).

Note that (**a**) and (**e**) are different. We do not reach the same result by applying operators (**1;2**) (**1;3**) to (**a**) as when we apply operators (**1;3**) (**1;2**). In fact, the product of the operators (**1;2**) and (**1;3**) is *non-commutative*, as with Heisenberg's matrices. This can be written symbolically in the form:

$$(1;2)\ (1;3) \neq (1;3)\ (1;2)$$

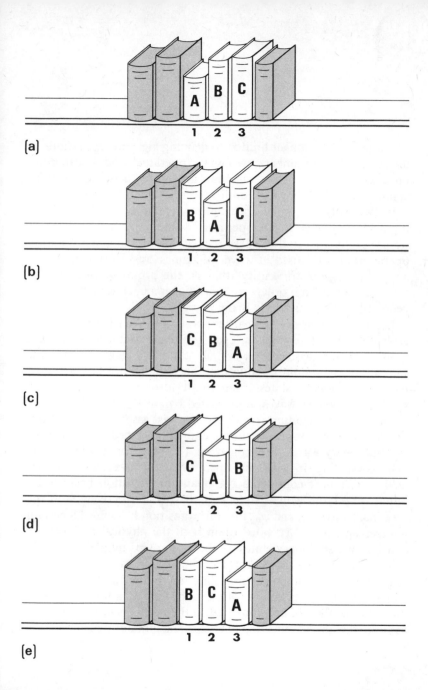

(a)

(b)

(c)

(d)

(e)

We are now no longer limited to defining algebraic operations in terms of ordinary numbers; we can use operators, and we can build up new operators. Also, algebras are more likely to be non-commutative than the more familiar commutative variety.

In his work on wave mechanics, Schrödinger related every physical parameter to an operator. Admittedly, these operators were very different to those described above, although permutation operators are also used in wave mechanics. Just as our operators act upon a geometric entity, that is, the group of three books arranged in a certain order, so Schrödinger's operators act upon a geometric entity which is de Broglie's wave.

Let us now go back to an earlier paragraph. We have seen that to each quantum state (that is, each stationary state of the atom), wave mechanics associates a certain stationary wave which is the solution of Schrödinger's equation. Since there must be a series of possible stationary states, there must also be a corresponding series of stationary waves, represented by $\psi_1, \psi_2, \psi_3 \ldots$.

But for each quantum transition, we must associate *two* stationary states of the atom: the initial state and the final state, that is, two stationary waves. Starting from a physical parameter, say **a**, and associating it with an operator which we shall call **A**, Schrödinger next considered the quantum transition between an initial state **i** and a final state **k**, associated respectively with the stationary waves ψ_i and ψ_k. For this transition he defined a certain number a_{ik}, which depended upon both the physical parameter **a** and the two stationary states of the atom. This number could be calculated by using the operator **A** and the waves ψ_i and ψ_k.

By considering all the possible quantum transitions, he calculated all the corresponding values for a_{ik}, and drew up a table in which, for example, the **i-th** line consisted fo the numbers $a_{i1}, a_{i2}, a_{i3} \ldots$ associated with the transitions between the initial state **i** and all the possible final states. Finally, Schrödinger proved that because of his choice of operators, his wave equation showed that the resulting tables were the same as Heisenberg's matrices. They obeyed the same laws, and they satisfied the same equations.

It was in this way that the calculations of wave mechanics could be translated into the language of matrix theory; Schrödinger had provided the equivalent of a dictionary. The formal mathematics of the two theories were linked, forming one scheme which can be called either wave mechanics or quantum mechanics.

More probabilities

We have now described how quantum mechanics was born and how two originally different theories were brought together. However, the two were not of equal importance, and in the end it was wave mechanics which proved to be more valuable. It was more adaptable and more profound, and its methods of calculation and reasoning were more sweeping, while those of matrix mechanics were used more modestly in order to carry out convenient analyses of certain problems. On the other hand, the concepts of probability, which had guided Heisenberg from the very beginning, soon became of prime importance.

Classical theory stated that the behaviour of a particle can be described in terms of two parameters, position and velocity. Scientists were quite used to handling these familiar properties. Wave mechanics, however, introduced only one parameter: the wave associated with the motion of the particle. The problem was to discover how all the results drawn from measurements of position, velocity and energy could be obtained from this single function. In trying to solve this puzzle, theorists began to introduce statistical laws in all manner of places. It was even stated that a wave of matter has itself a probabilistic significance.

Actually, this problem was not entirely new, because Einstein had already encountered it when he had put forward his theory that luminous energy is carried by photons rather than by waves. At that time he wanted to find out why the laws of propagation of waves could predict the behaviour of photons. To show what is involved, we must return briefly to the phenomenon of the interference of light.

We know that in an optical experiment, such as Young's, the idea of the superposition of waves explains the appearance of bright and dark strips. The bright strips correspond to the regions of maximum intensity of the wave, while the dark strips correspond to regions of minimum intensity. Yet if this is taken to provide a proper explanation of the phenomenon, we must also assume that the luminous energy occurring in space is proportional to the intensity of the wave. This hypothesis can be justified in various ways; all the same, it constitutes an extra concept, that of the *probability principle*.

Following Einstein, let us suppose that luminous energy is carried by means of photons. We must conclude that more photons will reach the bright strips than the dark strips, and therefore that the light-wave is controlled by the distribution of the photons in space. The photon density will be greatest where the wave is at its most intense. The wave now becomes much more abstract, since its role is to govern the statistical distribution of the photons.

Actually, this interpretation is still inadequate. This is shown by the fact that we can still obtain interference phenomena by using light so feeble that the photons reach the photographic plate one by one; with sufficient time of exposure, the bright and dark strips will appear as before. In this case, then, we are dealing with something more than the density of photons in the beam of light, and we must assume that *each* photon, considered individually, will tend toward the regions where the intensity of the wave is greatest. This is why Einstein, in his original researches, suggested that the intensity of the luminous wave at each point in space represents the probability of each photon being located at this point.

This probabilistic interpretation of the luminous wave was generalised by Max Born in wave mechanics. As we have already noted, waves of matter and waves of light have exactly the same properties of diffraction and interference; and interference experiments made by using electrons are equally successful when the stream is so weak that the electrons reach the interferometer one by one. It was natural to assume, with Born, that just as for light-waves, *the intensity of a wave associated with a particle is, at each point and at each instant, equal to the probability that the particle will be at that point and at that instant.*

This probability principle can be used to solve one of our problems, that of predicting the position of the particle from a knowledge of the wave. In order to find the other physical parameters, however, we must introduce a second concept, the *superposition principle.* To show the significance of this, it will be helpful to take the example of a beam of light.

If we know the colour and the frequency of a beam of light, we can assume that its photons are of the same frequency. But what happens if the frequency of the beam is not accurately defined, if, for instance, it is the result of the superposition of many waves of different frequencies?

By the use of a prism or a diffraction grating, the light can be split up into many different beams whose frequencies are known, and each beam will of course contain identical photons. By means of the probability principle, we can then work out the photon density from the intensity of each beam. On coming out of the prism, the number of photons of any particular colour will be directly related to the total intensity of the corresponding beam.

It seems that before passing through the prism, the photons already existed in the incident light. Their waves were superposed, and the relative intensities of the waves corresponded to the relative numbers of photons of each colour to be found in the original beam. Yet these relative intensities can be calculated before any actual measurements are made, and this means that we can also predict the distribution of the photons which come out of the prism. It can be seen that the intensities of the emerging waves, which represent only parts of the original beam, take on a new statistical significance affecting the frequencies of the particles rather than their positions. Nevertheless, this concept still proves to be inadequate.

Suppose, for example, that before reaching the prism the beam of light crosses a material medium which absorbs all the colours equally, so that the same proportion of photons is retained for each frequency. In this case, it follows that the individual waves of the beam will be weakened, but their relative intensities will stay the same as before. If the beam is very much enfeebled, it is possible that the photons will arrive one by one, and that each individual photon will be associated with a superposition of waves of differing frequencies. This means that we can no longer use a statistical interpretation of the wave, because this would be valid only for large numbers of photons. We must follow Born in supposing that the intensity of each of these monochromatic waves will give the *probability* that the photon will come out of the prism in the beam which corresponds to that particular frequency. We are therefore considering the probability that the final frequency will be the same as that attributed to the photon.

Let us now apply these ideas to wave mechanics, bearing in mind that the energy of a particle is related to the frequency of

28 In the case of a wave carrying a large number of corpuscles the square of the amplitude in a given region is proportional to the number of corpuscles contained within it.

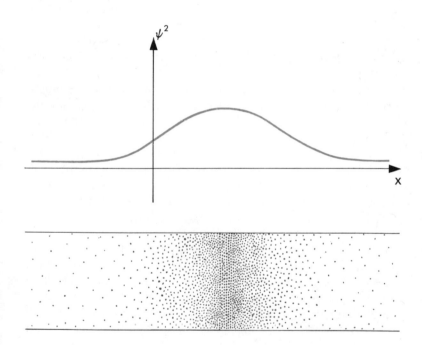

de Broglie's wave by the relation $E = hv$. If the frequency of the wave is well defined, then the energy of the particle will be equally well defined. In the case of light, however, the wave is generally the result of the superposition of many components of different frequencies. The superposition principle states accordingly that *the intensity of each of the partial waves of frequency v which arises as a result of the splitting up of the original wave is a measure of the probability that the particle will occur in a state whose energy is* $E = hv$.

We must now consider the relationship between these fundamental principles and Schrödinger's equation. First, applying the interference principle, the intensity of the wave over a small volume is a measure of the probability that the particle will occur within this volume, and therefore the sum of the intensities taken over the whole of space must be equal to the probability that the particle will occur somewhere. But this probability must be equal to unity, since we can be certain that the particle exists. This means that from Schrödinger's equations, we can select those which will give us a total intensity of unity – the so-called *normalised* solutions.

Remember that we have linked the quantum states of the atom with those particular solutions of Schrödinger's equation which give us the corresponding stationary waves. It is found that these stationary waves are the same as the normalisable waves, and so obey the probability principle. Moreover, it can be shown that *all* normalisable waves are produced as the result of the superposition of a certain number of stationary waves. Since a stationary wave corresponds to a well-defined value of energy (and therefore of frequency), it follows that the normalised waves are superpositions of waves each of which have a definite frequency. When the state of an atom is represented by a certain normalised wave (the solution of Schrödinger's equation), the frequencies of the stationary waves created by the splitting-up of the atom give the energy-values which can effectively be held in the atom itself, while the intensities of these stationary waves are linked with the probability that each of these different values can occur.

Thanks to these two principles, the results of any operation affecting position and energy can be predicted. But what about other physical parameters, such as velocity? To answer this question, we must delve deeper into abstract theory, and go back to Schrödinger's idea that each physical quantity can be represented by an operator.

Starting from any of these operators, it is possible to calculate a series of normalisable functions which are called *eigenfunctions*. Each of these eigenfunctions is associated with a number which is the corresponding *eigenvalue*. From this new viewpoint, we can see that the stationary waves which have been previously calculated from Schrödinger's equation are nothing more nor less than the eigenfunctions of the 'energy' operator, and that the quantum values for energies defined by the frequencies of these waves are in fact the corresponding eigenvalues. This leads to the general idea that if any physical parameter **a** is represented by an operator **A**, then the eigenvalues of this operator must be the quantised values which will occur when the physical parameter is measured.

Although all the *possible* values of any parameter can be predicted in this way, we still need to know the probability that any one or other of these values will actually occur. To achieve this, we make use of the idea of superposition which has already been successfully applied to energy, and generalise it for all physical quantities. Just as we have split up the compound wave into a set of stationary waves, so we now split this wave-function into a set of eigenfunctions of an operator **A**, which represent any physical parameter **a**. We can now lay down the *general superposition* *principle*, or degeneracy principle: the wave function which represents the state of a physical system can be split according to the eigenfunctions of an operator **A,** where the intensity of each eigenfunction equals the probability that a measurement of the quantity **a** will give an eigenvalue corresponding to the operator.

Harvest-time

It would take a whole book to describe all the harvest of results originated by quantum mechanics. At the time when the principles were being laid down, fundamental papers followed each other in quick succession, in fact, at a rate that has never been equalled either before or since. Admittedly, this avalanche lasted for only a few years, but for a short time it seemed that scientists had become demigods – able to overcome any obstacle. So let us now deal with what we may call the Golden Age of quantum theory.

Once again we must start with the atom of hydrogen, which played so great a role in the Bohr-Sommerfeld theory. In his original paper on wave mechanics, Schrödinger showed that the spectral frequencies of hydrogen followed directly from his equation, and later on he was able to calculate the corresponding intensities. These results were an important step in the success of his theory.

However, this calculation, like Bohr's original theory, was unable to explain the fine structure of the spectral lines. This cannot be regarded as unexpected, because we know from Sommerfeld's work that the fine structure is linked with relativity, and relativity does not enter into the theory. Attempts were then made to modify Schrödinger's equation so as to include relativistic laws, but, to the general surprise, these efforts were not successful. Though the resulting equation did indeed give a formula for the fine structure, the results were clearly wrong; they simply did not fit the observed facts.

The weakness of the theory was underlined by its inaccurate results with regard to the spectra of x-rays, and also for the influence of magnetic fields upon sources of light. The same troubles had plagued Bohr's original theory. It seemed that although the puzzle had been brilliantly re-constructed by means of the new mechanics, there was still a vital piece missing.

Actually, this missing piece had been found by two Dutch physicists, Uhlenbeck and Goudsmit, even before the beginning of wave mechanics. Since many of the properties of an electron are connected with magnetic phenomena, Uhlenbeck and Goudsmit came to think of an electron as a small electric charge that rotated on itself, as a top, so that it behaved in the manner of a small magnet. They gave the name of *spin* to this property of the electron, and when they introduced spin into Bohr's theory, they derived equations which went a long way toward clearing up the problems that we have just mentioned.

The main difficulty about quantum mechanics was that it did not include the Uhlenbeck-Goudsmit spin concept, or any substitute for it. The Swiss physicist Wolfgang Pauli therefore undertook the essential task of introducing it into the theory. For reasons which would take too long to explain here, he proposed to do this by giving to the electron not one, but *two* wave-functions, obeying a system of two equations very similar to Schrödinger's equation.

Although things were still by no means perfect, Pauli's equations did at least take into account the chief aspects of the unexplained phenomena. The low accuracy was not particularly worrying because Pauli had been able to introduce the spin idea only by disregarding relativity, and it seemed certain that this was the weakness of the theory. Unfortunately, there seemed at first no way of introducing spin and relativity into wave mechanics at the same time.

It was at this stage of the investigations that a remarkable piece of work was carried out by the quiet young Cambridge professor, Paul Dirac, who has already been mentioned in connection with his important contributions to matrix mechanics. He had a profoundly logical mind, together with deep appreciation of the abstract, and he was able to make a very strict analysis of Schrödinger's relativistic equation without worrying about the fact that its results did not agree with practical experience (actually, the agreement was very poor indeed). The equation was not in accord with the principles of probabilistic interpretation, since it even suggested that a particle might disappear without trace or be born out of nothingness.

Dirac tried to transform the equation so as to remove this anomaly, while at the same time remaining within the bounds of relativity laws. In this way, he arrived at a set of mathematical conditions which the so-called 'good equation' must satisfy. He showed that the required conditions could be realised only if *four* wave-functions were associated with the electron, obeying a system of four equations. These were *Dirac's equations*, and were found to give a nearly perfect description of the electron.

Although the idea of introducing several wave-functions had been inspired by Pauli's work, Dirac had never made a conscious effort to include the spin in his equations; nevertheless, there it was. Neither had he tried to account for all the phenomena mentioned earlier in this chapter, notably the fine structure of the hydrogen spectrum. Yet everything was included, and so accurately that it took spectroscopists almost twenty years to detect a slight difference between Dirac's theory and practical results. Also, by interpreting certain paradoxical consequences of the equations, scientists concluded that the electron must have an *anti-particle*, differing from an electron only in that its electric charge must be positive instead of negative. Nowadays, this anti-particle is well-known, and is called the *positron*.

Some years later, Dirac's equations were used by de Broglie in a new investigation of the problems of matter and light. Although wave-mechanics was born when the idea of duality of waves and particles, already familiar in optics, was extended to the whole of matter, the equations given by Schrödinger and Dirac were unable to account for the properties of light, and so the photon was absent from their theory. This was why de Broglie set out to develop a *wave mechanics of the photon*.

He managed this by assuming that a photon is the result of the 'fusion' of a couple of electrically neutral particles of extraordinarily small mass, each of which obeys Dirac's equations. To represent the photon, de Broglie had therefore to introduce a set of sixteen wave functions governed by sixteen differential equations, and he showed that these equations were basically the same as Maxwell's classical equations, so that he provided a quite unexpected connection between the new mechanics and the old electromagnetic field. Unfortunately, his analysis was not entirely successful because the wave mechanics of the photon could not give a satisfactory answer to the problem of the emission and absorption of light.

In spite of the importance of this research into new equations of evolution, the main practical problems called for a theory dealing with systems of interacting particles. In his original papers, Schrödinger had described systems of this kind by means of a very abstract 'wave' which evolved in a many-dimensional mathematical space. Naturally, the equation which governed this 'wave' played a fundamental role in studies of those atoms which contain numerous electrons, and also in the analysis of the various properties of matter.

29 Paul Dirac (born 1902), developed Heisenberg's theory of quantum mechanics.

However, in order to give a precise description of the systems of electrons, Pauli had had to introduce a new idea which was as fundamental as it was mysterious: the *exclusion principle*. This stated that it is impossible for two electrons to occur simultaneously in the same quantum state. The principle gives a very simple explanation of the empirical laws which had been used to interpret Mendeleyev's periodic table according to the old theory due to Bohr, and it is also essential in the study of 'electron gases' which diffuse through the lattices of crystalline structures and are responsible for the thermal and electrical phenomena in solid bodies.

The description of these phenomena also meant that there would have to be an alteration in the statistical analysis that Maxwell and Boltzmann had given for the kinetic theory of gases, because the quantum properties of matter had now to be taken into account. The particles were therefore classified into two categories, according to whether or not the value of their spin led them to obey Pauli's principle. Dirac and the great Italian scientist Enrico Fermi discovered the statistical law relating to particles which do conform – electrons and protons, for instance – and which are known nowadays as *fermions*. However, other particles, such as photons and some types of mesons, do not obey the exclusion principle; they require a different statistical analysis, created by N. S. Bose and Einstein, and they are called *bosons*. It was from the Bose–Einstein statistics that we can deduce the black-body radiation law which had been given by Planck, and which had led to the great quantum adventure.

From this series of brilliant results, we have so far left out those which deal with the difficult problem of the interactions between matter and radiation. Remember that in describing the discovery of quanta, reference was made to the objection that might have been raised by a classical physicist, that is, that if matter emits or absorbs light by quanta, the intensity of the luminous waves must vary in a series of jumps, which goes against the laws of electromagnetism. Our classical physicist was quite right; quantum theory was forced to admit the objection, and then to try to explain it.

According to the principles of wave mechanics, an atom situated in a radiation field has, at each instant, a certain probability of absorbing a photon. When this happens, the photon will disappear, and the light-wave will suddenly decrease in intensity, simply because the total intensity is proportional to the number of photons in the wave. The opposite process can also happen: if the wave suddenly gains an extra photon, its intensity will increase.

Actually, the problem is rather more complicated than this. From Dirac's theory, amply confirmed by practical experience, it is known that the electron has an anti-particle, the positron. When an electron and a positron meet, the result is an 'explosion', where the two particles annihilate each other and disappear and are replaced by two photons of high energy. These photons can be annihilated in their turn, giving rise to electron-positron 'pairs'. During these interactions between matter and radiation, neither the electrons nor the photons remain constant in number.

A new branch of quantum physics, the *quantum field theory* was worked out to describe these phenomena. It was founded by Heisenberg, Pauli, Fermi and Dirac, and for many years was faced with grave difficulties. It was only after the second world war that Tomonaga, Schwinger, Feynman and Dyson – a new generation of theorists – managed to put it on a more satisfactory basis. Its most notable success was the detection of tiny differences between spectroscopic measurements and the predictions of Dirac's equations for the hydrogen atom, now called the *Lamb effect*. By now it

30 In this bubble chamber photograph can be seen, among other things, two electron-positron pairs appearing from invisible photons. The electrons with opposite charges diverge under the action of a magnetic field.

can be said that the quantum theory of fields can give correct predictions for all the interactions between photons and electrons.

Unfortunately, the same cannot be said for the host of so-called 'elementary particles', more of which are being discovered yearly. So far as elementary particles and the structure of atomic nuclei are concerned, the theory is by no means convincing. In spite of many brilliant successes by an ever-increasing army of theorists, many of nature's secrets are still closely-guarded, and it may even be that another scientific revolution is imminent. Be this as it may, we will now leave the question of science in the making and science in the future. It is time for us to look more closely at the analysis of the physical content of the mechanics of quanta.

4 Never look behind the facts

4 Never look behind the facts

The Fifth Solvay Physical Conference

When, at the beginning of this century, Ernest Solvay gave part of his fortune toward founding the International Institute that bears his name, he rendered a great service to science. At the time, scientists in general were not used to travelling long distances to attend conferences, and the Solvay Institute provided a convenient central meeting-point. Meetings between a few dozen scientists, in order to discuss some particular problem, were to play an important role in scientific development.

The Fifth Solvay Physical Conference will undoubtedly be remembered as the most celebrated of these meetings. The chairman of the conference was Lorentz, the last great representative of classical physics. Among those present were Einstein and all the other creators of quantum theory – Max Planck, Bohr, de Broglie, Schrödinger, Heisenberg, Born and Dirac – together with eminent physicists such as Bragg, Ehrenfest, Langevin, Compton, Debye, Brillouin and others.

From 24 to 29 October 1927, the scientists discussed *Electrons and Photons*. They analysed their recent achievements, dealt with the meaning of the new mechanics, and tried to visualise a new world concept in accord with the formulae of the triumphant microphysics. It was a task worthy of such a gathering!

It would take many pages to give even a résumé of the long and difficult discussions that took place, but some of the highlights of the conference should be noted here because they marked a turning-point in the history of science. The crisis facing classical physics, which had lasted from the beginning of the century, was finally over – or, metaphorically, the curtain had fallen at the end of the first act.

As soon as the conference began, Bohr emerged as the leader of a powerful group which included Born, Heisenberg, Dirac, Pauli and Kramers, who brought in a method of interpretation of quantum formalism. To them, the whole situation was quite clear. The main theoretical problems had been solved, and the practical difficulties would soon be disposed of also. Born even said: 'We consider that quantum mechanics is a complete theory, and that its fundamental hypotheses, both physical and mathematical, are not susceptible to further modification.'

They considered that the significance and the consequences of the theory were now fixed, as well as the basic hypothesis itself. It was agreed that, in Bohr's words, 'the meaning of the theory can be expressed only by what we call the quantum postulate', and that 'this postulate means that we must give up all idea of causal description of atomic phenomena in terms of time and space'. Born added that with regard to quantum theory, all that one should ask is that the theory 'must contain no contradictions, and that it must be able to predict the result of any possible experiment within its range without fear of ambiguity'.

The aim of the group was to accept the basic idea of quantum theory, to reject from the theory any quantity which could not be observed, and to abandon determinism. The system seemed outwardly strange, but coherent enough, since an answer could be given to any question that might be asked. The group could have adopted Goethe's aphorism – 'Do not look behind the facts, since the facts themselves make up the doctrine'.

In spite of its mathematical elegance, this abstract and formal scheme was greeted with scepticism by some members of the conference and even with open hostility by a few. The only effective opposition was provided by Einstein, de Broglie and Schrödinger. Of these three, one had been responsible for a theory of light based on a hypothetical particle, the photon; the two others had created a new mechanics by assuming the existence of a wave which cannot be detected by any practical means. As Boltzmann had done not so long before, they had proved that a theory can be created from facts which are not directly observable. It was natural, then, that they were instinctively out of sympathy with Bohr's concepts.

De Broglie and Schrödinger, in particular, had no reason to take the existence of quanta as the basis for their arguments. Their wave mechanics had originated not from the assertion that quanta existed, but from the question: 'Why do quanta exist?' However, their very aims turned out to be disadvantageous in the debate that followed. They were trying to give added force to the new mechanics, and in so doing they found themselves defending two entirely different points of view instead of a single theory. At the same time, they were faced with extremely difficult problems which did not worry Bohr's followers in the least since Bohr and his group simply denied that such problems existed. Einstein's sympathies were with de Broglie, and he opposed Bohr's concepts by means of objections which did at least show how peculiar these concepts were. Yet Einstein failed to upset the system because he could not show that there were any serious internal contradictions.

Since there was no other complete theory available, the Solvay Conference of 1927 therefore ended in victory for the group which came later to be called the Copenhagen School. It is true that their ideas were never accepted by Planck, Einstein or Schrödinger, not to mention lesser opponents, and although de Broglie did accept the ideas for a long time, he has returned to his original viewpoint since 1952. However, it is undeniable that Bohr's conception of quantum mechanics has been taught throughout the universities of the world for the last forty years, and nowadays it is usually thought that the original reasons for adopting it were fully justified.

Nevertheless, the authors propose to describe this interpretation in a rather elaborate way, which will show its strength and its merits without glossing over the problems that it raises. The concepts of the Copenhagen School should surely be too important to require any trumped-up evidence or over-simplification.

To measure is to disturb

Let us start by seeing how quantum mechanics was modified by Heisenberg so as to cause a drastic change in the problem of the observation of physical phenomena. For this, we must define a certain number of physical quantities which will represent the phenomenon under study, after which we must measure these parameters by means of suitable apparatus. This can be illustrated by considering the movement of a tennis ball.

Classical mechanics tells us that the movement of the ball can be represented by two parameters – the position and the velocity of the ball at any instant – and that a simple means of measurement would be to film the ball so as to note its position at equal intervals of time. Next, we must ask ourselves whether the movement of the ball is independent of our observation.

The answer is, emphatically, 'no'. We cannot film the ball in darkness, but as soon as we illuminate it, the light exerts a pressure on its surface, and the velocity and motion of the ball will be disturbed. Admittedly, in this case the effect is negligible, but the principle is clear enough. We cannot measure the behaviour of the ball without modifying it; in other words, *to measure is to disturb*. However, physicists did not realise this before our own century, because there were two excellent reasons why the effect played no part in classical physics.

The first of these reasons is purely practical, and the example of the tennis ball is typical; it demonstrates that for problems within the scope of classical physics, the disturbances introduced by measurement are so slight that they are swamped in unavoidable errors of observation, so that they cannot be detected.

The second reason is theoretical, and much more important. According to classical physics, it is possible, at least conceptually, to weaken the disturbance indefinitely. For instance, if light is a wave-motion, we can diminish its intensity as much as we like, and so lessen the amount of the disturbance caused. True, the imperfections of the emulsions and photographic apparatus will set a limit, but in theory we can extrapolate the results of actual experiments and deal with ideal readings in which the disturbances are infinitely small. Therefore, it is permissible to refer to the world as it is and not only as we see it.

If the laws of quantum physics hold good, the situation is very different, and Heisenberg showed that it is impossible, even in theory, to measure a physical quantity without causing a disturbance. More precisely, any attempt to improve the measurement of a parameter which characterises a system will have the inevitable result of disturbing the value of another parameter of the system. If so, then the connection between the world as it is and the world as we see it will become truly complicated!

What causes this change? Essentially, it is due to the introduction of the dual wave-and-particle idea in the measuring process. We can explain this by going back to the example of the tennis ball, where the theoretical problems are the same as those for a particle in the world of atoms, but where the practical results are completely different.

Again, our first step is to work out the position of the ball. It is known that the energy of the luminous wave lighting up the ball is not distributed uniformly within the wave, but is concentrated in

A. PICCARD   E. HENRIOT   ED. HERZEN   TH. DE DONDER

P. EHRENFEST

P. DEBYE   M. KNUDSEN   W. L. BRAGG   H. A. KRAMERS   P. A. M. DIRAC

I. LANGMEÎR   M. PLANCK   MADAME CURIE   H. A. LORENTZ

R. H. FOWLER

SCHROEDINGER   W. PAULI   W. HEISENBERG   L. BRILLOUIN

E. VERSCHAFFELT

A. H. COMPTON   L. V. DE BROGLIE   M. BORN   N. BOHR

EINSTEIN   P. LANGEVIN   CH. E. GUYE   C. T. R. WILSON

O. W. RICHARDSON

the photons, which will disturb the motion of the ball when they hit it; therefore, it follows that in measuring the position of the ball, we are bound to modify its velocity.

As before, let us try to lessen this disturbance. Up to a point this can be done by reducing the number of impacts, that is, the number of photons, and all we have to do is to weaken the intensity of the luminous beam, because the intensity is proportional to the number of photons. Here, however, classical mechanics fails us. The intensity of the light is no longer continuous, and it cannot be reduced indefinitely, because at least *one photon* must be kept; otherwise, it is impossible to obtain a photographic image.

During the measurement of the ball's position, then, there must be at least one hit from a photon. To reduce the disturbance even further, the only course is to weaken the energy of collision; in other words, lessen the energy of the photon. But according to Planck's formula $\mathbf{E} = \mathbf{h}v$, the energy of the photon is proportional to the frequency of the luminous wave. Therefore, we are forced to reduce the frequency.

Unfortunately, this is not the end of our difficulties. Since the wavelength varies inversely with the frequency, the wavelength increases when the frequency is reduced. When discussing the electron microscope, in the previous chapter, we saw that using a longer wavelength means that the image in an optical instrument will become less sharp. It follows that if we have to decrease the frequency of the light so as to reduce the disturbance to the ball's velocity, we are bound to end up with a bad image, in other words, a bad measurement of position. To obtain a good measurement of position, there is no choice but to use light of a short wavelength. This means a high frequency, and an energetic photon which will cause greater disturbance to the velocity.

Starting with a measurement of velocity instead of position will come to exactly the same thing in the end. Either we make a good measurement and obtain an accurate knowledge of the speed of the particle without being able to tell exactly where it is, or else we can make an accurate measurement of the position at the cost of interfering with the velocity.

This type of analysis was first applied by Heisenberg. He gave numerous examples, which were later repeated by Bohr, and the final conclusion was that the duality of waves and particles makes it impossible for us to find out the position and the velocity of a particle, at any one moment, with complete accuracy.

Heisenberg expressed the principle mathematically in his famous *uncertainty relations*. If we represent the position of a moving body **M** by its co-ordinates **x**, **y** and **z** along the three axes **X**, **Y** and **Z**, and if the velocity is given by the three components v_x, v_y and v_z along the same axes (figure 32), then Heisenberg's relationships can be expressed as

$$\Delta x \ \Delta v_x \geqslant h/m$$
$$\Delta y \ \Delta v_y \geqslant h/m$$
$$\Delta z \ \Delta v_z \geqslant h/m$$

where **h** is Planck's constant, and **m** is the mass of the body. These inequalities mean that if, for example, we measure the position of a particle along the X-axis with an error (that is, an uncertainty) of Δx, and the speed along the same axis with an uncertainty Δv, then the product of these two uncertainties must be at least equal to Planck's constant divided by the mass of the article. This means that if the uncertainties Δx, Δy and Δz become less, then the uncertainties Δv_x, Δv_y and Δv_z will become greater. In other words, the more we know about the position of a particle, the less we know about its velocity, and vice versa.

One final comment must be made. Clearly, it is the ratio between Planck's constant and the mass of the moving particle which limits

32 Werner Heisenberg (born 1901). He showed in his uncertainty relations that it is impossible to find out the position and velocity of a particle, at any one moment, with complete accuracy.

the accuracy of simultaneous measurements of velocity and position. If the distances are expressed in centimetres, the masses in grammes and the time in seconds, then so far as an electron is concerned this ratio is equal to about 7. Therefore, if the position of the electron is known to an accuracy of one micron, the velocity may have an error of at least 700 metres per second. For our tennis ball, on the other hand, the ratio is of the order of 10^{-28}, so that in theory we can measure simultaneously its centre of gravity to within a ten million millionth of a centimetre and its speed to within a ten million millionth of a centimetre per second. This kind of accuracy is so far above our experimental capabilities that, obviously, Heisenberg's relations are of no practical importance on our everyday scale, and in classical physics they can be ignored completely.

To know is to measure

Heisenberg's relations brought the ambitious dream of Laplacian determinism to an abrupt end. If it is impossible to know the position and the velocity of a particle at the same time, then not even the most brilliant scientific mind will be able to predict the course of evolution of the universe with any real accuracy. This means that the laws of the new mechanics will depend upon chance, which is one reason why they are expressed in terms of probabilities.

In retrospect, it seems that the old determinism was somewhat naïve. The idea of an intellect powerful enough to consider all the particles of the universe at the same time, with full knowledge of their laws of force and of how to make use of them, belongs rather to the realm of metaphysics. It does not fit in with the natural laws of classical mechanics, and yet for a long time it is undeniable that unwarranted extrapolations of such a kind affected the whole progress of physics. When they were rejected, the immediate problem was to find something to put in their place.

Heisenberg's relations themselves indicate the key to the situation. Up to now we have discussed them only with respect to a few practical experiments in measuring, but, rather surprisingly, it can be shown that they are also an essential part of the statistical assumptions of quantum mechanics.

According to a mathematical theory due to the work of Joseph Fourier at the beginning of the nineteenth century, the frequency of a wave can be found more accurately when the wave occupies a large region of space. More precisely, if Δx is the wavelength of a 'packet' of waves moving along an axis X, and Δv is the interval of the frequencies in the packet, then the product of these two parameters is at least equal to the velocity of propagation of the waves, V. This may be written as

$$\Delta x \, \Delta v \geqslant V$$

Let us take two extreme cases. If the wave-packet of waves is perfectly localised and is reduced to a point, it must contain all the frequencies of the spectrum. If, on the other hand, its frequency is exactly defined, it will have to occupy the whole of space! (Incidentally, this shows that a truly monochromatic wave is nothing more than an abstract concept).

The same is true for any wave-packet, and in particular it holds good for de Broglie's waves, which are associated with particles. Now, according to the requirements of wave mechanics, there is a certain probability that we can observe the particle anywhere in space where the intensity of the wave is not zero, and if we know that we can observe the particle before making a measurement, then the particle will have to be in some section of the range Δx of the wave-packet. The particle's position can be narrowed down only to an accuracy of Δx, and this length is therefore a measure of the *uncertainty* with which its position can be defined along the X-axis.

Similarly, if the frequencies of the waves making up the packet range over an interval $\Delta\nu$, we can predict the frequency of the particle to an accuracy of $\Delta\nu$. Since $E = h\nu$, the result for the prediction of the energy has an uncertainty $\Delta E = h\,\Delta\nu$. But as the velocity is linked unequivocally with the energy, it too will have an uncertainty of $\Delta\nu$. This can be expressed as a function of $\Delta\nu$, and if it is introduced into Fourier's inequality we at once find:

$$\Delta x\,\Delta v \geqslant h/m$$

which is Heisenberg's relation, or uncertainty principle.

It can be seen that Heisenberg's uncertainty principle is directly linked with the fact that the different physical quantities which characterise the particle are defined by the properties of a wave. It is then easy to connect these measuring operations to the two extreme cases of Fourier's relation, described above. In effect, by giving the exact position of the particle we are compressing the 'packet' of its waves into a very restricted volume of space, with the inevitable result that we lose all our information about the velocity of the particle. Conversely, if we want to measure the velocity with complete accuracy, the frequency of the wave will have to be defined. This means that the wave will extend over a large region of space, so that we will be unable to locate the particle. All in all, it is obviously impossible to measure a physical quantity without disturbing the motion of the particle and altering all our predictions about the other quantities.

The same conclusions can be drawn from matrix mechanics. The method is more abstract, but it is worth noting that Heisenberg first obtained his uncertainty relations from matrix algebra rather than wave mechanics. When he wrote that '$\mathbf{a} \times \mathbf{b}$' was not in general equal to '$\mathbf{b} \times \mathbf{a}$', Heisenberg was showing that the order in which the measurements of $\mathbf{a}$ and $\mathbf{b}$ are made is not immaterial, because the measurement of **a** can modify the predictions about **b** and vice versa. Once again we come back to the principle that measurements cause disturbances.

The problem begins to clarify. Evidently the uncertainty principle, the statistical character of the laws of quantum mechanics and the duality of waves and corpuscles, are nothing more than different facets of a single complex reality which we must do our best to interpret. There are at least two possible ways in which we can make further progress.

The first consists of trying to keep the concept of fundamental determinism, which would govern the movements of the particles and waves in the absence of any disturbances. The co-existence of waves and particles must play an essential role in this kind of determinism, which is very different from Laplacian determinism. It will have to explain all the probability laws of quantum theory as well as Heisenberg's relations, so that quantum theory becomes a new kind of statistical mechanics.

Both the present authors agree with this concept, for reasons which will be described in the next chapter. First, however, it is only right to present the other point of view, which is accepted nowadays by almost all theorists. We will see how the Copenhagen School introduced a radically new concept of physics, where statistical laws are an ultimate reality, where indeterminism is a fundamental fact, and where Heisenberg's relations put up a solid barrier against all our efforts to find out more about the workings of nature.

A preliminary question must be asked. Classical physics contains various statistical laws which have already been discussed at length in this book. The fact that these laws exist does not rule out determinism, which in such a case must be Laplacian determinism. On the contrary, this determinism makes it possible for us to express and understand the laws of probability. Why, then, cannot this be equally true of quantum mechanics, and why does the whole situation seem to be reversed as soon as we start considering quanta? There is no need to stress the importance of this question. It was clear from the outset that unless Bohr and Heisenberg could provide a satisfactory answer, all their efforts were likely to prove abortive. There is every reason, then, to examine their arguments very carefully indeed.

As soon as we accept the probabilistic principles of quantum mechanics, we must realise that there is a fundamental difference between these new laws and the old classical statistical laws. The discrepancy is due to Heisenberg's uncertainty principle, that is, the impossibility in principle of gaining an absolutely accurate knowledge of the position and the velocity of a particle at the same time. While the probabilistic character of classical predictions was more or less accidental, it becomes fundamental when we turn to quantum theory. In other words, chance in classical physics would be eliminated, at least conceptually, by improving our knowledge of the mechanical systems, but this is not the case with the new physics, where Heisenberg's relations are quite ruthless in limiting the practical utilisation of an eventual determinism.

All this seems to indicate that any 'hidden' determinism lying behind the probability laws of quantum mechanics would be destined to stay hidden for ever; its sole use would be to provide statistical predictions in conformity with the uncertainty principle. And yet what statistical predictions? Undoubtedly, those which are contained in the probability laws, and which are already known simply because they are in accord with practical experience and because they go as far as the uncertainty principle allows. So far as practical experiments were concerned, it would make no difference whether the predictions were due to 'pure' laws of probability, or whether the cause lay in some hypothetical hidden determinism.

The views of the writers of the present book will be given later. Meanwhile, it is worth noting that the great mathematician von Neumann took the idea to such an extreme that he even produced a theorem stating that it would be impossible to picture any hidden determinism which would reproduce the statistical laws of wave mechanics. This strange theorem claims that theory will not only explain all the observed phenomena, but will also, by way of its own internal logic, preclude any other explanation. However, de Broglie carried out a critical analysis, and showed that von Neumann's theorem was based upon an *ad hoc* hypothesis which in itself rendered the whole theorem valueless. We still cannot rule out the possibility of a hidden determinism.

This did not seem important to either Bohr or Heisenberg, who maintained that a hidden determinism would, at best, lead back to the statistical laws of quantum theory, so that practical experiments could not, in themselves, give a reliable answer to this particular question. They concluded that it must be possible to reason as though no such determinism existed. In other words, they decided *to adopt the probability laws of wave mechanics as the ultimate reality*, to admit that Heisenberg's relations were proof of the *fundamental indeterminism* of the laws of nature, and to re-cast our ideas according to these concepts.

It may be rather presumptuous to try to find out the reasons, other than rational arguments, which lead scientists of the calibre of Bohr and Heisenberg to make up their minds. All the same, it is worth making an effort to describe the ideas which made them take up a viewpoint so very far removed from the great traditions of physics.

When Bohr drew up the first model for an atom, he had no choice but to throw overboard many of the accepted laws of physics. His theory was founded entirely upon experimental results and, as we know, turned out to be extremely successful. The situation which led Heisenberg to his matrix mechanics was somewhat similar. He had to be even more systematic in his approach, since as far as possible, he selected only those physical parameters which could be directly measured. And it applied, too, to another of Heisenberg's great discoveries – the uncertainty principle, which came from his attempt to link theory with possible practical confirmation.

It is not surprising that Bohr and Heisenberg gained in confidence from their successes, and undoubtedly they had excellent personal reasons for believing that physical theory must beware of anything that is inaccessible to experimentation. And yet this is rather a matter of opinion. Dalton's atoms, Faraday's field, Einstein's photons and de Broglie's waves are examples of physical entities which were invented with no reference to experimentation, and their successes were just as brilliant as those of Bohr and Heisenberg. Nonetheless, Bohr and Heisenberg kept firmly to their philosophical assumption that theory must contain only concepts which have a practical signficance, and must keep to predictions which can be experimentally verified.

With this in mind, they developed an interpretation of quantum formalism which was logically coherent, and which was in accord with experimental results. Admittedly, there were certain questions which could not be answered, but this seemed to Bohr and Heisenberg to be a help rather than a hindrance; these particular questions concerned non-observable parameters, and so were dismissed as being quite without significance. Since their programme had been carried through, there was no need to complicate matters by bringing in any hidden determinism. Moreover, how could it be possible to find out whether such a determinism really exists, when we do not agree even about the meaning of the word reality? It was thought that so far as we are concerned, everything happens as though no determinism exists, so that the question solves itself.

According to the Copenhagen School, then, there must be an essential indeterminism, and Heisenberg's relations will become *relations of indeterminism* as well as of practical uncertainty. It is not enough to say that it is impossible to know the exact position and velocity of a particle simultaneously. It must be maintained that, in general, there is no such thing as a well-determined position or velocity. Matter and light become fugitive indeed, and any hope of representing the world in terms of pictures and motions becomes nothing more than an empty dream.

Corpuscles or fields

From the analysis given above, we shall retain the conclusion which implicitly contains the whole of the philosophy of the Copenhagen School: Heisenberg's relations are equations of indeterminism, so that in general a particle simply does not possess a well-defined velocity or position. The next step is to consider how this concept affects the two great probabilistic laws of wave mechanics, the probability principle and the superposition principle.

The first of these principles lays down that we may observe the particle at any point in space where its wave is not zero, since the intensity of this wave is equal to the probability of its being present. At first sight, it may seem natural to interpret this result by saying that the particle is in a definite position, but we merely do not know just where it happens to occur within its wave. Oddly enough, many physicists, even modern ones, have fallen into this trap, forgetting that it is in direct contradiction to Bohr's ideas. If Heisenberg's relations express *indeterminations*, it is meaningless to claim that the particle occurs 'somewhere' before being observed. We must realise that the particle occurs *at the same time* along the whole extent of the wave; it spreads itself in some manner from one region to another, with greater or less probability.

Similarly, the superposition principle states that the wave function is split up into a certain number of elementary waves, each of which defines a possible value for the velocity and therefore the probability of obtaining this particular value during an observation. Yet here again it is misleading to claim that an uncertainty has been introduced into our predictions. Remember that we do not know the actual velocity of the particle, all we have to guide us is a jumble of possible values. Following Bohr and Heisenberg, we must assume that before the measurement, the particle does not have a well-determined velocity, and all it has is a whole series of velocities *at the same time*, each of which has a probability of being observed. Analogous conclusions could be drawn for any other parameter, such as energy, but for the present purpose it will be best to limit our discussion to the fundamental physical quantities of position and velocity.

It is evident, in any case, that the word 'particle' no longer means the same as 'corpuscle', since a corpuscle is defined as a piece of matter or energy in some particular position. It is impossible to picture a corpuscle which has several different velocities and several different positions at the same time. In any case, according to the Copenhagen School, the corpuscular conception of matter must be given up.

If so, then can matter be pictured in the form of waves? This may seem plausible at first sight. If we represent a particle by a wave-packet, it will be an entity, but will not be limited to one definite point in space, and can exist simultaneously at many points. Unfortunately, there is one fatal objection to this idea. When a particle reaches some kind of apparatus (a photographic plate, for instance), it is never recorded as a series of waves: it behaves in the manner of a localised entity, or, in other words, a corpuscle.

Therefore, a particle is not a wave, because it can be localised during an observation. Neither is it a corpuscle, because before the observation it must be assumed to have a whole set of possible positions and velocities. It is neither the one nor the other; it is a combination of both. Yet the problem of representing a particle on its own had no real significance to Bohr and Heisenberg. They maintained that the classical concepts of the wave and the corpuscle are unable to explain the actual situation, even though both these concepts are essential, and they concluded that within the framework of space and time, it is impossible to give an unequivocal description of a particle. Moreover, if measurement involves disturbance, how can we hope to define a particle without involving the very measuring instruments that have to be used to prove the particle's existence?

The reality of an electron or a photon is linked with the sum total of the possibilities of obtaining certain results with the help of adequate measurements. We shall have a set of possible values for the measurements of position, and also for the probabilities of realising them; there will be similar sets as regards velocity, energy and so on. Note, however, that the statistical distributions relating to these various quantities have a curious property which can best be illustrated by means of an example.

Take a box containing six steel balls, of which one is black, and six clay balls, of which three are black. If we chose a ball at random, the probability of its being steel is obviously $\mathbf{P_f} = 6/12 = \frac{1}{2}$:

and the probability of the ball being black *when we already know that it is steel* will be $\mathbf{P_r}^{(f)} = 1/6$.

Similarly, the probability of our taking a black ball from the box will be $\mathbf{P_r} = 4/12 = 1/3$:

while the probability that the ball will be steel, *when we already know that it is black*, will be $\mathbf{P_f}^{(r)} = \frac{1}{4}$:

We can easily derive the following equation:

$P_f \times P_r^{(f)} = P_r \times P_f^{(r)} = P_{rf}$ (since $\frac{1}{2} \times 1/6 = 1/3 \times \frac{1}{4} = 1/12$) which simply expresses the well-defined probability $\mathbf{P_{rf}} = 1/12$ of our choosing a *black steel ball*. The ball exists objectively, whether we find it or not.

For a particle, we can define and calculate 'analogous' probabilities. For example the probability $\mathbf{P_x}$ of finding the particle at a point $\mathbf{x}$, the probability $\mathbf{P}_v^{(x)}$ that it will have a velocity $\mathbf{v}$ when we know that it is at $\mathbf{x}$, the probability $\mathbf{P_v}$ that it has a velocity of $\mathbf{v}$ in any case, and, finally, the probability $\mathbf{P_x}^{(v)}$ of observing the particle at $\mathbf{x}$ when we already know that it has a velocity of $\mathbf{v}$. But have we reached a formula similar to the first – that is,

$$P_x \times P_v^{(x)} = P_v \times P_x^{(v)} ?$$

The answer is 'no'. Simply because measurements involve

disturbance, our predictions must change according to the sequence in which we measure x and y. The probabilistic laws of quantum theory mean that we can no longer conceive a state in which the particle is at x with a velocity v, and which we can observe with a probability of P_{xv}. In any case, we could not record this state without violating the uncertainty principle.

It is seen, then, that the probabilities calculated in quantum mechanics do not correspond to the distribution of values of different physical quantities which have an objective co-existence, as is the case with everyday objects such as steel and clay balls. They have a meaning only with respect to an eventual measurement. This is what Bohr and Heisenberg were expressing when they said that statistical distributions exist only 'potentially', and that this potentiality is made effective by the measurement itself. *According to the Copenhagen School, the particle is only the sum of the 'potentialities of measurement' contained in its wave function.*

This is the fundamental conclusion resulting from the interpretation of Heisenberg's relations as relations of indeterminacy. It seems that the classical wave and corpuscle models have no place in this new physics, in spite of their countless applications in the past. However, Bohr tried to retain at least something of this method of interpretation, and he was led to his famous *complementarity principle*, which his followers often regard as the conceptual key to quantum mechanics.

Actually, the classical concepts of the corpuscle and the wave (taken in this case to mean 'monochromatic wave') are incompatible, and even contradictory. The wavelike aspect of matter and of light implies a wavelength, and hence a velocity, which is well defined, while to observe corpuscular properties we need to know the exact position of the electron or photon. Yet according to the uncertainty principle, we cannot know both velocity and position;

33 According to Bohr's interpretation, a corpuscle can only be localised to a point on the wave by measuring its position. It is 'potentially present' at all points on the wave and only by making a measurement can we make it appear at a single point and give a meaning to the world 'localisation'.

if we have a better knowledge of the one, we are correspondingly less sure about the other. This means that the corpuscular aspect will be recorded only during an experiment which makes it hopeless for us to study the wave aspect, and vice versa.

Consequently, Bohr was fully entitled to state that the concepts of wave and corpuscle will never clash in our description of nature, mutually contradictory though they admittedly are. This means that the problem of an insoluble choice will never occur. The electron or the photon will behave *like a wave in some cases, like a corpuscle in others* – sometimes resembling a corpuscle, at other times resembling a field – according to the experimental methods used in our observations. The concepts of the wave and the corpuscle were said by Bohr to be *complementary*, because both are essential in any description of reality, both are always potentially present to a greater or lesser degree, and each appears to the detriment of the other. According to Bohr, then, the velocity and the position of the particle are complementary.

Instead of the unequivocal description of nature that had been developed by classical physics, Bohr gave a description by means of couples of concepts or complementary variables; this, he maintained, was an inevitable consequence of quantum law. The two examples cited above (wave/corpuscle, and position/velocity) are the most important, but there are others, even though we sometimes arrive at nebulous statements such as the complementary character of 'causality and the space-time description'. Some efforts were made to extend these ideas into other disciplines, notably biology, psychology and sociology, but the results of these extrapolations were not very convincing, to put it mildly!

In spite of its lack of precision, the complementarity principle provides a language which is often useful in describing microsystems according to the ideas of the Copenhagen School. On the other hand, it should be borne in mind that even the framework of these ideas is not adequate to give a full interpretation of quantum formalism. In particular, it cannot solve the most delicate and controversial problem contained in the theory, known in theorists' jargon as 'the reduction of the wave-packet by means of measurement'. The question cannot be fully discussed here, but we can at least try to point out the salient facts, because the question is the centre of the orthodox interpretation of quantum mechanics.

Take the simple case of an electron of mass m, moving freely. At an instant t_0, we have some information about the electron. We know, for example, that it is to be found between points x_0 and $x_0 + \Delta x$ on the x-axis, and that it has a velocity somewhere between v_0 and $v_0 + \Delta v_0$. It is understood that Δx_0 and Δv_0 satisfy Heisenberg's relations

$$\Delta x_0 \ \Delta v_0 \geqslant \frac{h}{m}$$

All our knowledge about the state of the particle at the instant t_0 should be included in the expression ψ_0 of the wave function at that instant. Moreover, according to the probability and superposition principles, ψ_o must be a wave-packet which is enclosed in an interval of space $(x_o, x_o + \Delta x_o)$, and which, according to de Broglie's equation, contains all the wavelengths between

$$\lambda_0 = \frac{h}{mv_0} \text{ and } \lambda'_0 = \frac{h}{m(v_0 + \Delta v_0)}$$

This function, ψ_o, carries all our information about the electron, and therefore it constitutes the description of its initial state.

Once the form of the wave-packet at the instant t_o has been laid down, its development will be rigorously defined by Schrödinger's equation. It is precisely this deterministic evolution of the wave which allows us to predict the state of the electron at any later instant, and therefore to make statistical predictions about the result of measuring some physical quantity or other. In such a way we can, for example, calculate the intensity of the wave at a certain instant t later than t_o; according to the probability principle, we will then know the probability of finding the electron at any point in space where the intensity of its wave is not zero.

But suppose next that we want to test this prediction by making an effective measurement of the position of the electron at an instant t. We can detect the electron by means of a small spot at a certain point x on a suitably-arranged photographic plate, and we can then find out whether this point corresponds to our prediction that the intensity of the wave will not be zero. Repeat the experiment a great many times, with the electrons always placed in the same initial conditions, so that their state is always represented by the same wave-packet; a set of spots will appear at points x_1, x_2, x_3 . . . on the plate, and we can check the accuracy of the probability principle by confirming that the density of the spots in each part of the plate is suitably proportional to the calculated intensity of the wave. Remember that it is experiments of this sort which give reliable confirmation of a theory. This has been said before in this book, but is worth repeating simply because it is so important.

The difficulties start when we begin to consider any one of these individual measures of position. According to the Copenhagen School, an electron has no well-defined position before the measurement is made; it is 'potentially' spread over the whole of the space occupied by the wave ψ. We must ask, then, why it suddenly starts to behave as though it were an entity in a definite position. More explicitly, the measurement of the position of an electron – by means of a photographic plate, for example – leads to its representation as a very localised wave-packet, virtually corresponding to the dimensions of the small black spot which we see. Yet *before the measurement*, the electron was represented by *another packet of waves*, whose dimensions might well be very large. What we have to do is to understand how this packet of waves has instantaneously turned into a point.

Obviously, the immediate answer which, from Bohr's point of view, we can give to the shrinkage of this wave-packet (or, to give a better name, this *packet of probabilities*) is simply to blame the measuring apparatus, in this case, the photographic plate. Note that because of the existence of the constant **h**, we cannot observe a particle without disturbing its state. Gamow once said that in a world controlled by quantum law, one cannot stroke a cat without breaking its neck. On this view, it is the photographic plate itself which has caused one of the 'potential' localisations of the electron to become effective. In fact, the drastic reduction of the packet of probabilities is due to the interaction of the particle with the measuring apparatus.

Outwardly, this explanation is so attractive that it has been accepted by a great number of writers who claim to follow the ideas of the Copenhagen School. Unfortunately, its inadequacy is shown

173

34 Renninger's experiment.

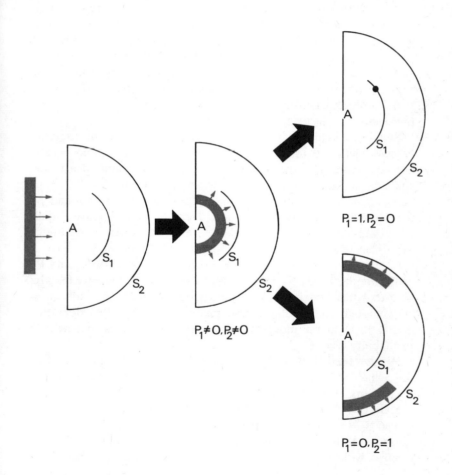

$P_1 \neq 0, P_2 \neq 0$

$P_1 = 1, P_2 = 0$

$P_1 = 0, P_2 = 1$

up as soon as we study what Renninger has called an *experiment with negative result*.

Imagine that we have an opaque screen in which there is a small hole **A**. In front of this hole, we place an obstacle such as a screen S_1, whose shape is that of the section of a sphere of radius r_1 and with its centre at **A**. Next, add a second screen S_2, of the same shape and with the same centre as S_1. The two screens S_1 and S_2 are coated with a substance capable of emitting a scintillation when struck by an electron. Therefore, the screens will register the presence of an electron.

Suppose that an electron coming from the left passes through the hole **A**. The electron wave ψ will undergo diffraction, and once it has passed through the hole it will take on the shape of a hemispherical surface centred on **A**. Over a period of time, it will expand like a soap-bubble, and it will advance at a speed which can be determined by practical methods. Here, it is this wave which constitutes the description of the state of the electron. As might have been guessed, we can predict that the electron will have a certain probability P_1 of hitting the screen S_1, and a probability P_2 of hitting the screen S_2. Obviously, $P_1 + P_2 = 1$, since we may be sure that the electron will go somewhere or other. Actually, it is easy enough to calculate these probabilities, but this does not matter to us at the moment; all we need to know is that neither probability is zero.

We can predict, with sufficient accuracy, what will happen after the instant **t** when the hemispherical wave-front reaches the screen S_1. Assume, first, that we observe a scintillation. This means that the electron has hit screen S_1, and so it cannot carry on to hit screen S_2. In other words, the probability P_1 that the electron will hit screen S_1 becomes equal to unity, and the probability P_2 that the electron will strike screen S_2 falls to zero. But the shape of the wave ought to express this change of state of the electron, and so it must be suddenly modified. We thus have a reduction of the packet of probabilities, and the analogy with our previous example is clear: the reduction is due to the interaction between the electron and the screen S_1, which may be regarded as the measuring apparatus.

Note, in passing, that the modification of the wave in this example consists of an *instantaneous* disappearance of the wave from all points in space except the point on the screen S_1, where the scintillation has been observed. This is a very curious behaviour for a physical phenomenon, as Einstein pointed out to the Solvay Conference by means of an analogous example. But suppose, on the other hand, that *no scintillation appears on the screen* S_1 as the hemispherical wave passes it. In this case the electron must have missed S_1, and will certainly hit S_2, so that now P_1 falls to zero and P_2 becomes unity. Again there is a reduction of the packet of probabilities by the measurement, yet what is really remarkable about it is that we have an example of a result shown by negative observation. All we have really done is to show that the electron *has not fallen on screen* S_1. It follows that strictly speaking, we can reach the same conclusion even if there has been no interaction between the object and the measuring apparatus. How, then, can we maintain that this interaction is responsible for the reduction of the packet of probabilities?

However, it is undeniable that in a more general way, the measuring apparatus does play a role in the process. It is clear that the presence of the screen S_1 is essential with regard to the change of shape of the wave function, even if its effect is not observable. On the other hand, it is equally obvious that the measuring apparatus does not in itself give an explanation of the phenomenon. Next, let us see how the orthodox interpretation combines the consciousness of the observer with the physical process.

35 The two initial systems 1 and 2, having interacted in
the region **R,** produce pairs of correlated states $1' - 2'$, $1'' - 2''$, etc.
If we consequently find system 1, for example, in state $1'$,
we can then expect to find system 2 in state $2'$.

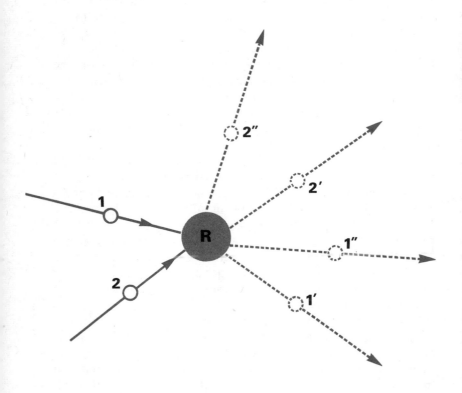

Consciousness and objectivity

We are now faced with a curious problem. Having accepted the idea due to Bohr and Heisenberg that theory can deal only with physical quantities that are actually observable, can we profit from the results of our measurements? This is the whole basis of the problem.

When we want to observe a micro-object, such as an electron, we must put it into contact with the material that makes up the measuring apparatus. This measuring apparatus is itself made up of protons, electrons, etc., which are subject to the laws of wave mechanics. This means that the interaction between the micro-object and the measuring apparatus is a process of interaction between two quantum systems, and Schrödinger's equation should be able to give us some general conclusions about it, in principle at least.

Calculation shows that the interaction leads to a series of *correlated* states of the two systems; that is, each possible state of one system corresponds to a possible state of the other. Therefore in the example given above the interaction of the electron with the screen S_1 will lead to two possible states of the electron; either it will hit a point on the screen S_1 or else it will remain potentially present over the whole extent of the wave which is moving toward S_2. These two states are correlated with two states of the screen S_1. Either it will show scintillation, or else it will remain blank.

It should be borne in mind that according to Bohr and Heisenberg, this description of the interaction given by the wave function is *optimal*. They maintain that a physical system is in itself its own wave function, because it contains all possible information about the system. This means that we can add nothing significant to this description without rejecting the whole interpretation of the Copenhagen School.

A measurement does not consist solely of an interaction between the object and the apparatus. A second phase, just as important as the first, follows at once. The observer examines the apparatus, decides that it is in a certain state, reasons that the object under study is in a state correlated with that of the apparatus, and then deduces the appropriate value for the parameter that he wants to measure. In our earlier example, suppose that the observer notes a scintillation at a point **P** on the screen S_1; from this he will conclude that the electron is located at that point, which gives him the position. After this, all the other states of the electron, which had originally been possible, are no longer available, since the observer now knows the state of the system. In fact, the increase in information has abruptly modified the packet of probabilities.

This seems so simple that we may well lose sight of the difficulty. Observing the measuring apparatus increases our information – after all, this is the purpose of the apparatus! – and so gives a more precise description of the system, which in turn implies a reduction in the packet of probabilities. But note that according to the Copenhagen School, our description was already optimal *before* we observed the measuring apparatus. How, then, can we claim that we are increasing our knowledge of the system, since this knowledge was already complete?

Consider the question from another point of view. In the previous experiment, it is not entirely proper to say that it is the interaction with screen S_1 (that is, the measuring apparatus) that has reduced the packet of probabilities, because this interaction leads only to a representation of the electron by two waves corresponding to two possible states (either the electron has hit S_1 or else it is moving toward S_2). We are entitled to discard one of these two possibilities, because of the knowledge gained as a result of the measurement which has reduced the group of probabilities. The reduction comes, then, from the information which we are introducing into the calculation, and which allows us to specify the state of the system. Are we then sure that the description of the process of interaction, by means of the evolution of the wave, is truly optimal, in other words, is it *complete?*

We can now see the importance of the problem. Nobody will deny that the microsystem can be described as being 'within a wave'; neither can we seriously question its probabilistic interpretation. And yet to follow the Copenhagen School, and claim that the description is complete, raises doubts in the minds of many leaders of contemporary physics. The whole question has led to various arguments which still remain undecided. But before going into the orthodox interpretation of the measuring process, it will be worth illustrating the previous discussion by means of an objection raised by Schrödinger in his amusing *cat paradox.*

Suppose that a cat is tied in such a manner that it will inevitably be hit by the bullet of a rifle whose trigger is electronically controlled by an instrument capable of being operated by the arrival of a single photon. The instrument is placed behind a semi-transparent mirror, so that part of the incident light will be allowed to pass through and part of it will be reflected. The whole is placed inside a sound-proofed opaque box (so that nobody may know what is happening inside). The box has one opening, through which a photon can pass. Let us now try to predict the result of the experiment.

At first sight, we seem to be faced with two possibilities. Either the photon will be reflected by the semi-transparent mirror and nothing will happen, or else the photon will go through the mirror and operate the mechanism which fires the rifle, so that the cat will be shot. Before we open the box, it is impossible to know whether the cat is alive or dead; but there is no doubt that it must be one or the other, whether we can observe it or not!

According to Schrödinger, the orthodox explanation is quite different. When the photon reaches the mirror, we cannot know whether or not it crosses it. Accordingly, we must conclude that the photon has 'potentially' crossed the mirror, and that it has been 'potentially' reflected. In the first case the cat will be dead, and in the second case it will be alive; but since the two states of the photon co-exist 'potentially', Schrödinger maintains that according to the orthodox interpretation the cat is both 'potentially dead' and 'potentially alive'. It will then be the observer who will be responsible for the possible death of the cat, simply by opening the box, since this action will bring about one of the states which is potentially present.

Supporters of the Copenhagen School, such as von Neumann, disagree with this opinion. Von Neumann looks at the general problem of measurement in the following way. The reduction of the group of probabilities does not depend only upon the interaction between the micro-system and the measuring apparatus; it also implies the existence of an observer, who has to look at the result as recorded by the instrument. But the observer himself is made up of atoms and molecules, and can be described as a physical apparatus. Therefore, instead of looking at the *object – measuring-apparatus* relationship, we must consider the logical extension: *object – measuring-apparatus – observer*. It is this triple relationship which causes the reduction of the group of probabilities.

Yet if we look 'objectively' at the evolution of such a system, we can see that it brings out no new qualitative conclusion. Quantum formalism will simply lead to the prediction of a triple set of correlated states of the object, the measuring-apparatus and the observer. It will not lead to anything that can affect the reduction of the packet of probabilities, and so is anything to be gained by adding the observer to the system?

36 Schrödinger's cat paradox. A photon entering through the opening **O** may be reflected at the semi-transparent mirror **M** and become absorbed and cause no subsequent action. Alternatively, it may pass through the mirror and register on the electronic apparatus **E**, which then activates the mechanism **C** connected to the trigger of the gun **F**. The box is assumed to be lightproof and soundproof.

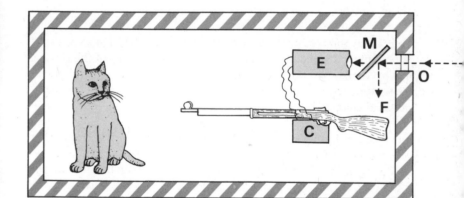

Von Neumann considers that we have reached a situation that is qualitatively different, because, unlike the object and the measuring-apparatus, the observer has an 'introspective faculty' or 'conscious-ness', which makes him immediately conscious of his own state. Once he knows this, he will also know the state of the apparatus, and hence that of the object. He can therefore proceed with the reduction of the group of probabilities. To quote London and Bauer, who were von Neumann's most famous interpreters: 'During the measurement, therefore, the occurrence of a new ψ in the system is not due to any mysterious interaction between the measuring apparatus and the object. It is simply due to the observer's consciousness of himself, which is separated from the old function ψ and which constitutes a new objectivity, on account of its conscious observation, thereby giving the object a new wave function.'

Regarding this conclusion, de Broglie says in one of his books: 'I have quoted this text, but I do not understand it at all well. This "consciousness" which is separated from the wave-function seems to be much more mysterious than the interaction between the object and the measuring apparatus could ever be.' He also recalls Schrödinger's ironical play upon words: 'The theory of the ψ wave has become a psychological theory.' Using the term 'metaphysical' in its etymological sense, it is in fact impossible to ignore the metaphysical character of such an explanation.

Von Neumann is able to answer the question as to how we can increase our knowledge when it is already complete. He claims that our knowledge is not, in fact, really complete, since it takes no account of the 'conscience' or the 'introspective faculty' of the observer. However, it must be added that we are assuming the possibility of a quantum description of the observer simply by including him in the system. Theoretically, of course, we can claim that the hypothesis of an optimal description of matter by the ψ wave is not affected by an 'introspective faculty' that must be outside the scope of the theory. Yet if so, we may be justifiably surprised that an interpretation so closely attached to its principles that it cannot bypass the experimental possibilities of measurement, must finally be forced to take into account the existence of a personal factor which, by definition, is beyond the scope of the theory.

During the last few years there has been a renewed surge of interest in these long-forgotten problems. Even inside the framework of orthodox ideas, serious efforts have been made to revise and extend the theory of the measuring process. The most ambitious of these attempts aims at explaining the reduction of the group of probabilities by the macroscopic character of the measuring apparatus, but up to now the attempt has been unsuccessful. In fact, it seems that these efforts cannot succeed, because although we can virtually disregard the practical difficulties, the conceptual difficulties remain as great as ever. It looks rather as though von Neumann's theory will remain as the only significant answer within the framework of the ideas of the Copenhagen School.

Whether von Neumann's theory seems attractive or not, we must appreciate its internal logic, and agree that it has produced coherent answers to all the objections ranged against it. Several of these objections have been described here, but it is worth saying something more about one particularly famous problem: *the paradox of Einstein, Podolsky and Rosen*, another example of an ideal experiment which tends to underline the incomplete character of Bohr's interpretation.

Einstein and his collaborators start by making it clear that they believe in an objective reality which is independent of human knowledge. They cannot give a full account of this reality; after all, it is science's task to discover its various facets, little by little, but they do lay down the following criterion: 'If, without causing any disturbance in a physical system, we can predict with certainty the value of a physical quantity with which it is connected, then we must conclude that this quantity corresponds to an element of reality.'

Admittedly this is a postulate, even a philosophical one, but it is laid down in terms which are so general and so cautious that it would seem difficult to disbelieve it. In particular, the caution implied in the words 'without causing any disturbance in the physical system' means the rejection of any case in which the measuring operation itself gives to the system a physical quantity of the amount predicted. Of course, anything of this kind would render the whole measurement quite meaningless.

Leaving this question for the moment, and returning to the problem of quanta, let us next consider another ideal measurement. Take a molecule made up of two atoms **A** and **B**, and examine a certain physical quantity for each of them, such that for each atom it can adopt values of only $+\frac{1}{2}$ or $-\frac{1}{2}$. Any quantity would do; but it will be convenient to consider the *spin* of the atoms, which is comparatively easy to visualise. Suppose that either the spin of **A** or the spin of **B** is unknown, but we do know that the spin of the molecule, that is, the sum of the spins of **A** and **B**, is zero.

By means of a process which does not disturb the spins in any way, separate the atoms until there is no chance of any interaction between them. Measure the spin of **A**, and suppose, for example, that it is found to have a value of $-\frac{1}{2}$. We can then be absolutely sure that the spin of **B** has a value of $+\frac{1}{2}$; and this prediction can be made without any disturbance of atom **B**, which is too far away to be affected. According to the criterion of Einstein, Podolsky and Rosen, the spin of **B** has therefore the character of an *element of reality*, and since the measure made of **A** has had no influence on **B**, we must conclude that **B** already had a spin of $+\frac{1}{2}$ *before* we measured the spin of **A**. Our measures of **A** have increased our knowledge about the spin of **A**, and hence our knowledge of the spin of **B**; but it has not modified the element of reality, that is, the spin of **B**.

Yet according to the Copenhagen School, at the start of the experiment each of the atoms is 'potentially' in a state of spin of $+\frac{1}{2}$ and 'potentially' in a state of $-\frac{1}{2}$; these two sets of potentialities are correlated by our knowledge of the total spin. It is by measurement of the spin of **A** that the atom acquires a specific spin, and this means that the spin of **B** becomes defined immediately. Therefore, before the measurement of **A**, Bohr could not properly discuss the spin of **B**, which existed only 'potentially'. To Einstein, Podolsky and Rosen, on the other hand, this spin is an element of reality, because it has a specific value all the time, even if this value is unknown. Therefore, according to this viewpoint, Bohr's interpretation does not contain all the elements of reality, and must be regarded as incomplete.

Bohr answered this objection by the simple method of refusing to accept the criterion. Without denying the existence of a reality, or even the possibility (at macroscopic level) of splitting up this reality into elements capable of being measured individually, Bohr rejected the idea that such analysis would still be valid at quantum level. While Einstein, Podolsky and Rosen were trying to demonstrate the incomplete nature of the orthodox interpretation, basing their arguments on this particular criterion, Bohr was claiming that the success of his theory showed the criterion to be inadequate. His attitude was understandable enough; nothing else would have been consistent with his overall interpretation.

And yet these various discussions did not disprove the arguments of Einstein and his colleagues. It was certainly quite in order for them to use a criterion which was clearly contained within the framework of classical physics and relativity theory, and it had not been shown that an interpretation such as that favoured by the Copenhagen School was necessary. Those who followed Einstein felt that the inadequacy of Bohr's interpretation had been effectively demonstrated. Almost twenty years later, Einstein wrote as follows:

'There is such a thing as a "state of reality" of a physical system, existing objectively, independent of all observation and measurement, and capable of being described by means of the normal language of physics . . . . This idea about reality cannot be clearly expressed in itself, because of its "metaphysical" nature; it has merely the character of a "programme". All scientists, including those engaged in quantum research, accept this idea about reality until they start to discuss the fundamentals of quantum theory. For example, nobody doubts that the centre of gravity of the Moon occupies a specific position, although there are no observers there, either real or potential. Let us then consider this theory of reality in a logical and arbitrary manner, without trying to evade its consequences. In this sense, I am not ashamed to put the concept of "the real state of a system" at the very centre of my considerations.'

5 God is strict, but He is not unkind

5 God is strict, but He is not unkind

What else can we do?

We have now seen how the edifice of quantum theory has been built up. We have seen how Planck, Einstein and Bohr built the first floor upon the firm foundations of classical physics – a floor which was as peculiar as it was novel. Later the new builders, de Broglie and Schrödinger on the one side and Heisenberg, Born and Dirac on the other, constructed two extra floors which were quite unlike each other, but which were integrated into the same structure in a way that seemed almost miraculous. Finally, Bohr covered the whole building with a strange roof which reflected a brilliant and unexpected vision of the world. Once the building was completed, people became used to its style, and it was seen to be in harmony within the city of science.

We could either end our book at this point, or else go on to mention some of the most recent developments of the theory. For example, something could be said about the still mysterious forces which unite protons and neutrons within atomic nuclei, so making these nuclei stable. Another fascinating topic concerns the new fundamental particles, whose life-spans are ephemeral, and which can be studied when they are produced by powerful synchrotrons or in cosmic radiation.

Very naturally, these problems have occupied the attention of thousands of physicists over the past thirty years, and the research has taken up a great deal of money as well as mental effort. Undeniable progress has been made, and there can be no doubt that further discoveries will follow, but, frankly speaking, it seems that the progress achieved has not measured up to the tremendous efforts that have been and are being made. The optimism of those first years has been somewhat dampened, and new ideas are needed. There have even been questions as to whether quantum theory has exhausted itself, and whether it will ever regain its original energy.

This pause in theoretical progress, and the problems that persistently arise, are sufficient to justify a detailed critical examination. Is quantum mechanics, as we know it, capable on its own of evolving beyond the principles upon which it was founded? Will the new ideas now being sought do nothing more than improve the existing theory, or will microphysics again undergo some dramatic change in aspect?

If we take a close look at quantum mechanics, we are forced to agree that most of the facts upon which it is based appear to be unshakable. There is no doubt that the existence of Planck's constant, the duality of waves and particles, and the quantised states of atoms correspond to strict physical reality. And in view of the extraordinary number of phenomena predicted and explained by Schrödinger's equation and the probability postulates associated with it, it would be tempting to consider the mathematical methods involved, as a necessary consequence of the basis of the whole of quantum theory. We are left with the roof of the building, the interpretation developed by Bohr and the Copenhagen School, which does not seem to have the same solidarity as the rest. Since it is open to criticism, it leads to queries about the whole of quantum theory, and hence it may well be that matters are not so simple as they seem.

In this book, we have tried to explain how Bohr and Heisenberg drew up their interpretation of quantum formalism, and we have done our best to show the coherence of their point of view. No attempt will now be made to attack the logic of their system, or the fact that their vision of the world is so remote from everyday experience. Ultimately, it may be found that an analysis at the level of microphysics simply cannot be made without accepting the theories of Bohr and Heisenberg; after all, a vision of the world need not be false just because it contradicts some generally-accepted ideas.

What we may bring to this interpretation is a philosophical postulate which is, in effect, a certain conception of the role and structure of physical theories. We already know this conception: theory must contain no physical quantity or prediction which cannot be linked with some experimental result. It was this principle that finally led to the general belief that de Broglie's wave is not a material wave, but simply a wave of probability which allows the prediction of the results of measurements. It is what may be called an 'element of prediction'. It was this same principle which led Bohr and Heisenberg to their conclusion that the present formalism of quantum mechanics is the inevitable consequence of the duality of waves and corpuscles.

Working according to sound scientific methods, it is clear that we do not need to know whether the philosophical assumptions of the Copenhagen School are true or not. All we need to admit is that like every philosophical assumption, they have no demonstrative value in themselves, in spite of their logical agreement with the calculations of quantum mechanics and the great discoveries that have been made in their name. We must now try to find out whether, starting from other postulates just as 'arbitrary' as Bohr's, we can construct a new interpretation of quantum mechanics, and if so, whether any different theory would lead to new results. In other words, can we find something different, something even better?

Generally speaking, the question seems pertinent enough, and such an undertaking would be worth while, since we cannot afford to neglect any possibility. However, a physicist could put forward two objections which merit close study.

He could say, for example, 'I am quite ready to admit that it would be possible to give an interpretation of the formalism of quantum theory which is based on ideas quite different from those of Bohr. But since the predictions of quantum mechanics have always been found to be valid, the results of any practical experiments you might make would necessarily be the same as Bohr's, which means that your new vision of microphysics would not amount to a new theory, even though it might provide scope for philosophical argument. Moreover, if you arrive at your interpretation by introducing parameters which cannot be confirmed by experiment (a procedure which Bohr could never accept), you are bound to submerge your theory in a morass of unverifiable assumptions. So why make the attempt?'

It must be admitted that these arguments are plausible, and account largely for the hostile reception of any proposals to reinterpret wave mechanics. Yet there are many cases in which the same kinds of arguments have been used in scientific history and have been refuted. A new interpretation of a physical entity or a mathematical formalism will produce not only a fresh vision of the world, but also a new theory, involving results which may not contradict those of the older ideas but which will be totally beyond their scope. To make this novel interpretation, it may be necessary to introduce hypothetical physical entities which cannot be measured as yet, but may be directly studied at some future date. History shows that this sort of thing has happened often enough in the past.

It is easy to give many examples which illustrate the role of the interpretation of a physical quantity in theoretical physics. For a long time, heat was regarded as an indestructible fluid, the 'calorie', which was supposed to be transmitted from hot bodies to colder ones – a fruitful picture which led to Carnot's principle. However, thermodynamics changed its aspect, and became the science that we know today, when heat became accepted as a form of energy, and the principle of equivalence was introduced. Similarly, light waves were once thought to be vibrations in a material medium, the ether. This idea seemed to be in accord with Fresnel's theory, but the interpretation of light-waves as electromagnetic vibrations, together with the triumph of Maxwell's theory, produced a host of new results which led eventually to the discovery of relativity. Even Maxwell's theory was simply an extension of Faraday's concept of the field, which gave a real physical meaning to the electric and magnetic lines of force which (like de Broglie's wave nowadays) were regarded as abstract mathematical entities, or 'elements of prediction'.

Atoms themselves are examples of entities which were introduced arbitrarily into a theory even though they could not be observed. After a long and difficult struggle, the kinetic theory of matter prevailed in spite of thermodynamics, or rather in spite of the thermodynamicists! Whereas classical thermodynamics appeared to be very solidly founded, the kinetic theory had the disadvantage of having an inductive character and of being forced to introduce a great many hypotheses. For some years these hypotheses seemed to do no more than confirm the results of thermodynamics, and the new theory came into its own only when it showed itself capable of predicting new phenomena. In any case, there is no reason to believe that two constructions differing so markedly in their ideas and methods must always lead to the same predictions.

Statistical mechanics, which evolved from the kinetic theory, did not lessen the value of thermodynamics, which remained supreme in its own domain. It did, however, provide a greater under-standing of the laws of nature, and science benefited accordingly. Without these methods, nothing would have been heard about the black-body problem which led to Planck's constant, and it is doubtful whether quantum theory would ever have been developed.

Similarly, it is questionable whether a new microphysics would be able to replace the present methods of quantum mechanics, methods which have been used so extensively and so successfully. Initially, at least, the new microphysics might seem pointless when compared with the deductive reasoning already in use. Yet it might well provide a clue to the physics of tomorrow – a suggestion which may seem rather presumptuous, but which certainly cannot be ruled out.

It is worth remembering that at the end of the last century and the beginning of our own, at a time when physicists were pre-occupied with their fascinating experiments with cathode-ray tubes and with radioactivity, a major role was played by those research workers who were trying to disperse Kelvin's two dark clouds by investigating the shortcomings and the mysteries of classical physics. Nowadays, when the theory is marking time, similar research is needed, especially as quantum mechanics, despite its power and elegance, is still far from attaining the degree of purity reached by classical physics after three hundred years of thought.

It may be claimed that historical analogies are of no practical significance, at least in the present context, because we are faced with a situation which has no precedent (though can it truly be said that any historical situation has a precedent?). The objectors may go on to point out that the uncertainty principle limits our description of nature in a way which simply did not come into classical physics. And they may hold that past examples are therefore irrelevant, because there is no hope of our making any progress beyond the present theory.

Of course, nobody doubts the importance of the uncertainty principle, but it may nevertheless be possible to make progress by following a different approach. Not too much should be read into the uncertainty principle, and the present authors, at least, do not accept the absolute and almost mystical character that is so often attached to it. Eventually, it will be possible to give experimental confirmation of parameters and phenomena which are beyond the range of the theoretical methods available to us at the moment. This question will be further discussed below.

Such confirmation must certainly be found sooner or later. Any physical theory, however settled it may appear, is always open to change, because it is very difficult to take count of all the physical and mathematical hypotheses contained in it, and it is equally hard to decide how much confidence can be placed in them. On the other hand, it is even more difficult to estimate the role played by these various hypotheses in the long-term conclusions to be drawn from the fundamental principles of the theory. We must always beware of jumping to conclusions.

A physical theory is sometimes regarded as comparable with a slab of mathematical marble, but this is incorrect. The conclusions to be drawn from a theory do not always stem from its basic fundamentals; they often come from less well-defined assumptions, generally after the solution of equations which have been written down during the analysis. This is why Bohr's statement – that his interpretation of the formalism of quantum theory is an inevitable consequence of the duality of waves and particles – must be regarded with a certain amount of suspicion.

It would be encouraging to cling to the hope that there is no physical law that will set a limit to our knowledge of nature. This optimistic philosophy was well summed up, in allegorical form, by Einstein. His comment is engraved on the stone hearth of the reception room at the Fine Hall, the famous mathematical institute at Princeton University: 'Raffiniert ist der Herr Gott, aber boshaft ist Er nicht' – *God is strict, but He is not unkind.*

Corpuscles and fields

Let us now turn to the ambitious programme originally proposed by de Broglie shortly before the Solvay Conference of 1927 – and to which he has recently returned with the collaboration of a research group. Its chief aim is to find out whether, within the statistical laws of wave mechanics, we can visualise microphysical particles as synthetic entities, capable of being diffracted by obstacles in the manner of a wave, but nevertheless having well-determined position and velocity – that is, behaving also like a corpuscle. In other words, can we reconcile the apparently opposite concepts of energy fields and corpuscles of matter, and can we restrict Heisenberg's relations to the *uncertainties* of measured results instead of applying them to the indeterminism of the behaviour of particles?

It may be helpful to go back to Young's experiment, mentioned in chapter 1. Now, however, we assume that the light-source is so weak that the photons reach the apparatus *one by one*, as was actually done by Taylor in 1909. Under these conditions, Young's phenomenon of interference will not be immediately evident. Each photon will either cause scintillation or else make a spot on the detector, but at first these spots will seem to occur at random. As their number increases, however, it will be noticed that the spots tend to favour certain regions, where they will appear in great numbers, and to avoid other zones. Gradually the dark and light bands will appear, just as happens when stronger light-sources are used.

The first conclusion to be drawn from this experiment is that the observation of *one* particle indicates the presence of a *corpuscular* phenomenon which has a strictly specified position. This idea is confirmed by many other phenomena, such as the trajectories of particles in photographic emulsions, and the effects seen in a

Wilson cloud chamber. It is frankly difficult to maintain that the particle is 'sometimes a wave, sometimes a corpuscle' without being even more exacting than Bohr, who refused to consider any quantities which were not observable. In fact, we can observe only the particle, never the wave.

This is not to say that we can regard particles as 'classical corpuscles' whose overall statistical properties only are regulated by a wave. The duality of waves and corpuscles has a definite meaning, as can be shown by a very simple analysis which is often used to support the theories of the Copenhagen School.

All we need do is to apply a modern version of the argument used by Young himself against the emission theory, that is, the theory that light is purely corpuscular. If, in the experiment already described, we block up one or other of the two holes through which the photons are passing, the statistical distribution of the impact points will be completely changed, and the light and dark bands will disappear. Yet if the photon were a 'classical corpuscle', it would pass through one hole without 'knowing' whether the other hole were open or closed, so that blocking up one hole would merely reduce the intensity of the observed phenomenon without altering its nature.

This seems to indicate that if the particle does have a permanent, narrow corpuscular region, it must also have an extended aspect which will explain the phenomena of interference. But since these phenomena consist of a particular distribution of the impact points on the observation screen, it is natural to assume that the two aspects of the particle are closely linked, so that the motion of the corpuscular region is *guided* by the extended aspect. Since the extended aspect covers both holes in Young's experiment, it follows that a particle passing through one of the holes will be deflected differently according to whether the other hole is open or shut.

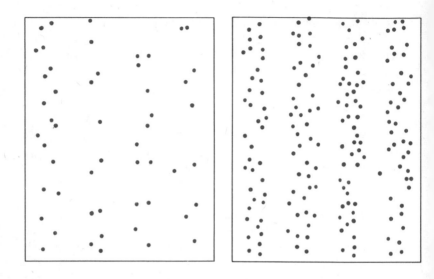

37 Successive images on the screen of an interferometer which is placed in the path of a very weak stream of particles. At first, the points of impact seem to be distributed randomly, but finally they indicate the existence of a statistical law which, in this case, corresponds to the appearance of the well-known dark and light bands.

38 De Broglie's conception of a particle as a 'wave with a hump'.

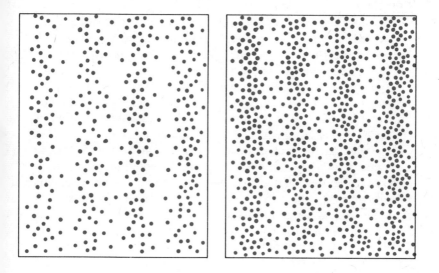

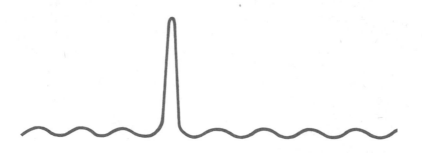

Finally, since the existence and position of the interference fringes is predicted with equal correctness by both optics and by wave mechanics, it seems that the extended aspect *of each particle* must be analogous to the waves upon which our reasoning is usually based.

Although de Broglie agreed with Bohr and Heisenberg that the classical models of waves and particles were inadequate, he did not think that it would be impossible to give a complete description of a particle; instead, he proposed a new model. His conception of a particle was that of a *wave with a hump* – that is, a wave whose amplitude is not regular over its whole extent, but comes to a marked peak in one particular region. This is represented schematically in figure 38, where the 'height' of the wave corresponds to its amplitude and its 'length' to its distribution in space.

If we assume that the energy contained in an element of volume of the wave is proportional to the square of its amplitude, then it is not hard to understand why the energy would be almost entirely concentrated in the so-called *singular region* marked by the hump. To keep everything as straightforward as we can, we may suppose instead also that the wave has an infinite value at the centre of the hump, thereby localising the particle at a point which we will call the *singularity*. Unlike an ordinary wave, it will carry a *localised corpuscle of energy*, and it will be this corpuscle alone which will be recorded by the photographic plate or other measuring apparatus; this, of course, will explain why we seem to be dealing with corpuscles. However, the wave will retain its extended character, so that it will be diffracted by obstacles and will produce the familiar interference phenomena.

It is interesting to note that these singular waves were introduced simultaneously in wave mechanics and in relativity. In 1927, the year of the celebrated Solvay conference, Einstein came to the conclusion that a material body cannot be considered as an entity distinct from a gravitational field, but simply as a region of very great intensity – a *singularity* of the field. From this, he derived one of the neatest results of general relativity. He showed that it is no longer necessary to lay down a law of motion for a body of this sort which would be analogous to Newton's $\mathbf{F} = \mathbf{m}\gamma$, because the law would follow directly from the equations of the evolution of a field which Einstein himself had discovered twelve years earlier. In other words, he discovered, without resorting to any other hypothesis, that the singularity representing the material body is *guided* by the gravitational field.

It can be seen that if the development of the wave is governed by Schrödinger's equation, we cannot, in wave mechanics, obtain a result similar to that of Einstein. This is because the equation has a restrictive property or 'linearity' – absent from Einstein's equations – precluding any close link between the motion of the singularity and the field.

At first glance, it might be thought that de Broglie's attempt is subordinate to the discovery of a wave equation more general than those already known. In principle, this is true; but the very success of Schrödinger's equation and of its relativistic generalisations suggests that they remain valid at least outside the restricted region which surrounds the singularity. It should therefore be possible to deduce the guiding of the corpuscle from the linear equations of wave mechanics. But in other to do this, we must first ask whether these equations do in fact have singular solutions which, contrary to the 'regular' waves used until now, will have infinitely large values in a very restricted region. The answer to the question is 'Yes'; the solutions will be called $\mathbf{u}$. (They satisfy only the equations of evolution outside the singular point, but this causes no difficulty).

The amplitude of these singular waves decreases very rapidly once we move away from the singularity, and it never coincides with the forms of the usual regular waves which exhibit the interference phenomenon. But because of the linearity of Schrödinger's equation, the sum of the two solutions is itself a solution. This is why de Broglie was able to represent the wave-hump **u** in the form

$$u = u_o + v$$

where $\mathbf{u_o}$ is a singular wave and **v** is a regular wave whose *mathematical* properties are essentially the same as those of the usual ψ wave. It is denoted by a different letter because it has a different meaning; it represents a field of energy similar to Maxwell's electromagnetic field instead of a 'potentiality of measurement'. Consequently, its amplitude will no longer be subject to the condition of normalisation referred to above.

It can be seen that the wave **u** as defined in this way certainly does suggest the image of the duality of waves and particles. Near a singularity the amplitude of the wave $\mathbf{u_o}$ is much greater than that of **v**, so that we can write approximately $\mathbf{u} = \mathbf{u_o}$, and the corpuscular aspect overrides the wave aspect. On the other hand, at a greater distance from the singularity the wave $\mathbf{u_o}$ decreases rapidly; the wave **v** does not decrease in the same manner, and so the wave aspect becomes dominant.

At this stage in the argument we come up against yet another problem because of the linearity of Schrödinger's equation. This linearity allows us to represent the humped wave in the form $\mathbf{u_o} + \mathbf{v}$, but it is not sufficiently accurate, because it imposes no choice on the two component functions, and so, in itself, it does not imply any connection between the wave aspect and the corpuscular aspect. The next thing we must do is to establish this connection.

De Broglie found this link by using the same idea that had guided him in his original studies in wave mechanics. He regarded the corpuscle as the site of a periodical phenomenon whose oscillation kept in phase with the regular wave which accompanied the motion. Since the particle was represented by the singularity of the wave $\mathbf{u_o}$, de Broglie naturally assumed that the same kind of phase relationship must exist between the waves $\mathbf{u_o}$ and $\mathbf{v}$. In other words, the two waves must vibrate in unison.

This principle sets considerable restriction on the choice of singular solutions, and, moreover, it connects them unequivocally with the regular waves. There is no longer any need to look for a singular solution except one that is *in phase* with the regular waves that are available. Mathematical researches carried out during the last few years have shown that de Broglie's solutions actually exist and can be found.

To sum up the physical analysis developed along these lines: *Any particle will be represented by a wave* $\mathbf{u}$, *which is the sum of a singular wave* $\mathbf{u_o}$ *and a regular wave* $\mathbf{v}$, *where both waves have the same phase and each satisfies the usual wave equation of wave mechanics.* Because of the association between singular and regular waves, de Broglie called his theory 'the theory of the double solution'.

A purely statistical concept of nature can be added to the fundamental hypothesis on which this model of the particle is based. First, however, we must discuss some of the consequences of the humped-wave concept; we must show that it leads to a new dynamics of particles which is more general than Newton's classical corpuscular dynamics. To simplify the explanation, it will be helpful to use what is called the *hydrodynamic image* of wave mechanics, first proposed a long time ago by Madelung.

Madelung noted that it is possible to put Schrödinger's equation in such a form that a regular solution $\mathbf{v}$ or ψ can be replaced by a *fictitious fluid*, whose density is given by the square of the amplitude of the wave and whose flow velocity is given by a certain function of the phase. But just as a wave is completely defined by its amplitude and phase, so the motion of a fluid is determined by its density and its flow-speed. If used carefully, this hydrodynamic image can provide an intuitive method of expressing some of the more abstract laws of wave mechanics.

Consider a cork floating upon the surface of a regularly flowing river. It will follow a certain path, and its speed at any instant will be well defined. It can easily be shown that this motion depends both on the place where the cork first entered the water, and upon the flow of the water. The movement will be the same each time we put the cork into the water at the same point, but if the original positions are different it will be found that the subsequent motion will also be different. This is because only one *stream-line* can pass through any one point on the surface of the river.

In any case, it is clear that the cork does no more than prove the existence of these stream-lines, each of which depends solely upon the flow conditions. If, for example, we put a large stone somewhere in the river, the water will have to go round it, with the result that the stream-lines will be deformed over a wide area. Consequently, if we now put the cork back into the water in the same position as before, it will follow a different path; it will be affected by the presence of the stone even if it never comes into direct contact with it or, for that matter, even if it never goes anywhere near it.

Let us now go back to de Broglie's humped-wave interpretation of wave mechanics, and apply two solutions of Schrödinger's equation, using the extended regular wave v and the localised singular wave u_o. Starting with the regular wave, we can picture Madelung's 'mathematical' fluid, whose density at each point is equal to the intensity of the wave v, and whose flow-speed is given by the phase. Just as with a real fluid, we can then use the velocity to define the stream-lines; they too will depend on the 'flow conditions' and, in particular, on the limiting conditions. And just as a stone distorts the flow-lines of the water, so a suitably-placed screen affects the propagation of the wave.

The abstract fluid describing the wave **v** must, somewhere or other, have a localised inhomogeneity which corresponds to the singular region of the wave u_0. Obviously, it is important to find out just what will happen. Since we have assumed that at this point the phases of u_0 and **v** are the same, and since the phase of **v** determines the flow-speed of the fluid, then the singular region must also have the same speed. In other words, the singularity of the wave u_0 must follow the stream-lines of **v**, just as the work followed the stream-lines of the river. Once we have accepted the principle that the phases of u_0 and **v** must be in phase, we can establish this result by means of a very general hypothesis – the *theory of guidance*.

From this representation of the particle by a humped wave, de Broglie was able to put forward a dynamics which was much more general than classical corpuscular dynamics. Since the energy of the particle is almost entirely concentrated in the singular region of the wave **u**, this region will behave like a localised corpuscle, following a well-defined path – or at least, because of its restricted spread, a very narrow tube of trajectories. It will resemble a classical corpuscle, too, in that its movement will depend upon known forces such as those of electricity or magnetism. Unlike the classical corpuscle, however, the singularity will be guided by the extended wave, and it will be subject to the effects of the diffraction of this wave over any obstacles even if a long way away.

Everything in this new dynamics behaves as though some new force is added to the classical forces acting on the corpuscular region. This new force is due to an energy potential unknown in Newtonian mechanics; it has been given the name of *quantum potential*, and we now know how to express it mathematically.

Although very different from classical dynamics, the new version does still regard the particle as an objective entity which exists independent of any measuring process. As against Bohr's image of the complementary properties of wave and corpuscle, the theory shows that it is possible to consider the particle as a complex entity which is always well defined. It follows that the duality has become a synthesis – both localised and extended, and both a corpuscle of matter and a field of energy.

More and more probabilities

The new dynamics of corpuscles and waves is drawn from the model of the wave with a hump. In principle it is deterministic. This determinism is very much richer than that of classical mechanics, but there is no hope of its being able to govern the behaviour of particles entirely on its own. It can manifest itself only in an indirect way because, as we shall see, it means that we shall be forced to reject the mechanistic hypothesis of a universe which obeys a finite number of laws. In this sense, our position becomes more radical than that of the Copenhagen School, and though the probabilities that we are considering will never be 'pure', they will inevitably appear everywhere.

Classical determinism assumed implicitly that it is possible to study physical systems as if they are isolated, or at least as if their interaction with the rest of the universe can be defined with complete precision. In practice, this is more or less true, but the idea may be considered as rigorous for macroscopic systems. The exact predictions of celestial mechanics are made on the assumption that the Solar System is isolated, and even in ballistic calculations it is usually good enough to neglect the interactions between the projectile and the medium in which it moves.

On the other hand, such predictions cannot be made with the same accuracy when we come back to microphysics. Consider, for instance, a photon wandering in the neighbourhood of a micro-system. We must take into account the irregularities of the surface of the microsystem, the thermal agitation of bodies which are regarded as inert, the weak interactions between adjacent mole-cules, and so on. There are many other examples of perturbations which upset the orderliness of the theoretical representations which are the basis of the determinism of pure probabilities. It is painfully clear that the idea of an isolated microsystem is very far removed from reality, but we are forced to admit that there must be a deeper level of reality in which atomic systems are in a state of never-ceasing fluctuation. This will be called the *subquantum medium*. The laws of quantum mechanics, then, cannot by themselves be a complete system, and any efforts to include them in a mechanistic scheme will be doomed to failure in advance. The statistical character of quantum laws provides us with an example of the endless complexity of natural phenomena, rather than a funda-mental indeterminism.

The properties of this subquantum medium are of great value as the starting-point for a new 'hidden' thermodynamics of particles. More will be said about them later. Meanwhile, let us now try to bring the effects of all kinds of perturbations into our description of microsystems.

Since every force-field can be expressed by the presence of an energy potential in Schrödinger's equation, the simplest way of representing these perturbations seems to be to introduce extra potentials, generally weak and of short duration. We know that we can describe the movement of a corpuscle on its wave by equating it with the motion of a inhomogeneity which flows along the stream-line of the 'fluid' as defined by Schrödinger's equation.

Some of the properties of this fluid, such as its conservation, do not depend upon the potentials introduced into the equation; on the other hand, they do affect the shape of the stream-lines.

Therefore, if a disturbing potential appears, the stream-line followed by the corpuscle will be momentarily deviated. When the disturbing potential ceases, the corpuscle will again follow one of the stream-lines of the undisturbed fluid, but this stream-line will not be the same as the first, If, then, the corpuscle is subject to slight but frequent fluctuations, it will seem to *'jump' constantly from one stream-line of the unperturbed fluid to another.*

Because of their very nature, it is impossible to give a detailed description of these fluctuations. Both the perturbations due to the subquantum medium and those produced by the interactions between atomic systems must be regarded as random, and this means that the jumping of the corpuscle will also be a random process. Even a knowledge of its initial position would be of little value, because the motion at any given instant could not be predicted with any exactness. All we could find out would be the *probability* of it occurring at any particular point.

But what will this probability be? According to the probability principle, which has been so completely confirmed experimentally, the probability must be everywhere proportional to the intensity of the wave v. We could try to arrive at this result from the probabilistic theory of Markov chains, giving certain statistical properties to the perturbations; but for the moment, let us try to justify it by returning to the analogy of the behaviour of a macroscopic fluid.

A liquid such as water is made up of molecules in a state of constant thermal agitation, so that the stream-lines followed by a body such as our cork represent only the mean motion of the liquid. However, it is much too large to be sensitive to the thermal agitation, so that no random motion will be detectable. Things are different with a very small object, such as a *colloidal micella*, an example of which may be given by the globules contained in milk visible under a microscope. Also, there are the particles of gutta-percha which Jean Perrin used in his studies of what is known as *Brownian movement*.

The Brownian movement shows that each corpuscle is subject to small random movements, so that there is no possibility of our being able to predict just what direction the motion will take at any particular moment. The stream-lines of the fluid will be followed only *on average*, and the corpuscle will continually 'jump' between the lines. Even if we know its initial position, we can do no more than calculate the *probability* that it will later occupy a particular place.

It follows that if we put a drop of milk into the water, the milk will slowly diffuse because of the random motion of its globules, until finally reaching a statistical equilibrium distribution which will be independent of the original positions of the globules. The mean number of globules in a specific volume of the liquid will therefore be to all intents and purposes proportional to the mass of water concerned; in other words, the chance probability of the presence of a globule will be virtually proportional to the density of the water. This brings us back to the probability principle in wave mechanics, since the intensity of the wave **v** which gives the probability of presence, or probability density, of the corpuscle is simply the density of the fictitious fluid defined by Schrödinger's equation.

This analogy is admittedly limited, and no demonstrative value can be given to it, but the connection established between the random fluctuations and the distribution of the probability densities is an ordinary postulate of physics. In fact, the probability principle is the second important prop of de Broglie's theory. It provides the

39 The blurred objects in this photograph are the tracks of
latex spheres in water viewed down a microscope — the well-known
Brownian movement (the bright spots are stationary spheres adhering
to the glass slide). Brownian movement cannot be explained by
classical thermodynamics — only by the kinetic theory of matter.

statistical element that was so obviously lacking in the humped wave
model, and it leads on to a reliable link with experimental results.

To see how this concept helps in an understanding of the basic
problem, let us return to Young's experiment which, as we know,
is so vital to the idea of wave-and-particle duality. This time,
however, we hope to interpret the phenomena by describing the
behaviour of particles in space and time.

When a particle reaches our opaque screen with its two holes, the
corpuscle-singularity, which is strictly localised, passes through one
of the holes (we do not know which). The wave **v** passes through
both holes at the same time, and on the far side of the screen it
gives rise to two waves which interfere with each other in the usual
manner, producing the light and dark bands on the detecting plate.
Yet if the amplitude of the wave **v** is very slight, its energy will be
insufficient to make the bands visible on the plate.

But from the probability principle, we know that the corpuscle
has its maximum probability of falling on the bands where the
intensity of the wave **v** is greatest. The particles that arrive later will
behave in the same way, except that in general they will hit the
plate in different positions. Initially they will appear to be scattered
around at random; but as their numbers increase, the distribution
will be governed by the wave **v**, and the bands will materialise in
front of our very eyes. Moreover, although the random motions
make it impossible to calculate the exact motions of each corpuscle,
we can nevertheless specify the stream-lines of the wave **v**, which
join the two holes to the observation plate. This means that we can

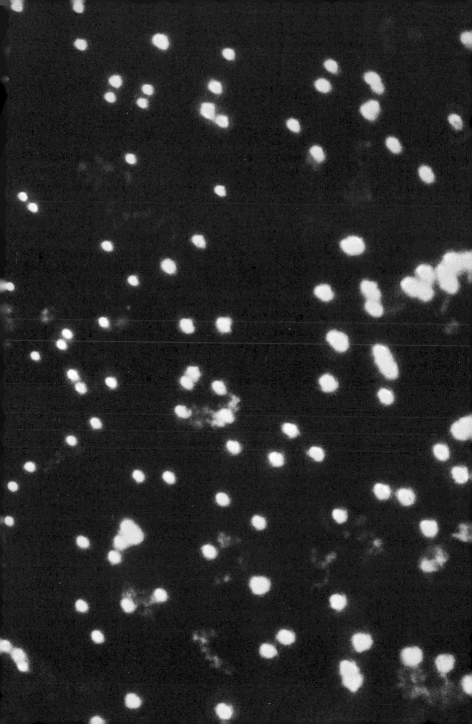

find the bundle of trajectories on which the corpuscle will be found for most of the time.

It is just as easy to interpret what happens when one of the holes is closed. Both the wave and the singularity pass through the hole that remains open, and calculation shows that the intensity of the wave **v** is virtually the same over a large area of the detector plate. There is no longer any reason for the impact-points to be grouped in definite bands; on the contrary, it may be assumed that the distribution of the spots will be practically uniform, and this is in fact precisely what is observed. Calculation of the stream-lines shows that there is a cone of trajectories, defining the motion of the corpuscles.

Analysis of these experiments and others of the same type shows that the humped-wave model really does contain all the ingredients for a synthesis of the corpuscular and wave aspects of matter and light. Up to now, however, we have dealt only with the probability density of the corpuscle, in other words, its position parameter. Other physical quantities, such as velocity and energy, play an equally important role in the theory, and we must see how their properties can be predicted, and how we must introduce the corresponding operators. To answer such questions we must briefly introduce a new conception of the measuring process.

It has already been shown that once we can specify the position of the corpuscle on the wave **v**, de Broglie's guidance theorem can define the velocity very accurately. The principal physical quantities can be expressed as a function of position and velocity, and these definitions will be the same as in classical mechanics except that they will take the existence of the quantum potential into account. Since velocity is specified by position, and the other parameters are determined by position and velocity, it follows that all the properties of the corpuscle can be perfectly defined

40 According to de Broglie, the corpuscle exists, at every instant, at a well specified point on the wave, which is, however, unknown to us. The measurement of the position will only specify the condition occurring at a particular instant out of the set of all the possible eventualities **(a)**, **(b)**, **(c)**, **(d)**, etc. Compare this with figure 33.

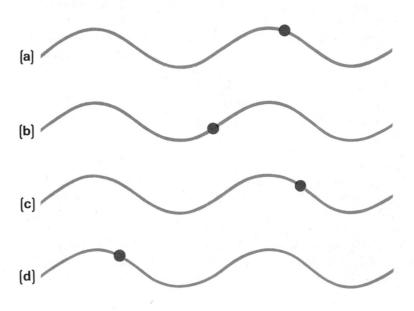

(a)

(b)

(c)

(d)

once we know the exact position of the corpuscle on the wave **v**.

Unfortunately, however, we do not know this position – because of the continuous jumping effect caused by the random fluctuations. Although the parameters of the corpuscle can be determined for any particular instant, the values are bound to change constantly in a way that simply cannot be predicted. This means that for velocity, energy or any other quantity, all we can do is to calculate the *deduced* statistical distribution, using the distribution of the probabilities of presence.

From the manner in which these distributions are defined, it is evident that they are not incompatible; their statistical character expresses only the *uncertainty* of our knowledge about the physical quantities, though of course the quantities have an objective existence. In wave mechanics, then, we have come back to a situation fully analogous to that of the steel and clay balls described on page 166.

But now we seem to meet with a serious difficulty. The ball example was cited to show how the situation differs from what we find in wave mechanics, where we have to introduce distributions of position and velocity which *are not compatible*. Now that this incompatibility has disappeared, it means that the new distributions are not the same as the old; more precisely, the distribution of the probability density stays unchanged (because it is always given by the probability principle). Yet the distribution of velocities deduced from the theorem of guidance cannot coincide with that drawn from the superposition principle; and since this principle is fully confirmed by practical experiments, it is tempting to conclude that the new conception is a failure.

As a matter of fact, we must reverse the problem. Since the distribution of velocities drawn from the superposition principle is incompatible with that obtained from the positions, then it seems that these two distributions cannot both correspond to the same objective state of the particle before measurement. If we want to describe such a state, we must modify at least one of the distributions. This is not surprising; it simply means that the distribution of velocities before measurement is not the same as the one we observe. Of course, we still need to understand why this is so, but from the general structure of the theory it is possible to deduce the exact statistical predictions of the measuring process, which were only postulated by the superposition principle.

As a first point, note that the measurement of any physical quantity in microphysics always leads back to the localisation of a corpuscle. It may be that this localisation is not that of the actual particle being studied, but that of many other particles which are interacting with it. The analysis of these different cases would not, however, add anything to the general reasoning, and so for the sake of simplicity it will be convenient to keep to the fundamental problem of a measurement which is obtained by the localisation of the particle itself.

The measurement of position is obviously the simplest. A detector is placed in the path of the group of waves, and by observing the scintillation at a given instant we can record the position of the corpuscle. There is nothing at all mysterious about this observation, since it means merely that the corpuscle is always localised and has arrived at the screen at that instant. This is an objective fact, and the 'consciousness' of the physicist does not come into it. It is independent of any observer, real or potential.

From this measurement of position, can we find out anything about the velocity of the corpuscle at that instant? In principle, the answer is 'yes', since we have enough knowledge about the wave v to allow us to find its phase at the point where it is recorded, and the guidance theorem then gives us the speed of the corpuscle. It seems that the whole problem is solved, and that we now know the position and the velocity *simultaneously*. Yet in practice, this is not so.

Our knowledge of the position of the corpuscle is affected by given uncertainties, and all we can really say is that we have narrowed it down to a set interval in space. If the phase of the wave v varies much in this interval, there will be a very large uncertainty in the deduced velocity, and all our information about the position will have been wasted. In other words, we can obtain an exact value of the velocity only when our knowledge of the position is independent of the actual spot on the detector screen where the impact occurred. This means that our value for the velocity will become more accurate when the phase variation of the wave v becomes less. Obviously, the best kind of wave for this purpose will be a monochromatic one.

There is only one way to obtain such a wave: we must first split up the incident wave v by means of a prism or some such device, and then put a detector screen in each of the emerging beams. When this is done, we can come back to our theoretical conclusions, and it is found that the results are in good agreement. It is important to note that spectral analysis is brought in not because of an *a priori* postulate, but because of the experimental necessity of making our measures of velocity insensitive to positional errors.

Almost the same reasoning can be applied to any measurement of a parameter which depends on velocity (such as energy or momentum), and it can be shown that the values obtained during the measurements – whose accuracy we are always trying to improve! – really are the eigenvalues of the usual *operators* in quantum mechanics. Here again, neither the eigenvalues nor the forms of these operators have been postulated *a priori;* they follow from the model of the particle obtained from the theory of the double solution and from the physical analysis of the measuring process. Finally, from the probability principle alone it is easy to deduce that these appropriate values appear in the observations only according to the probabilities given by the superposition principle.

The analysis given here has been all too short, but in conclusion it seems necessary to underline the essential influence of the fluctuations upon the prediction of the behaviour of a particle, even when we have an exact knowledge of the position and the speed at a given instant. If the phase of the wave **v** varies so slowly in the space that the speed of the corpuscle will be practically the same at any point on the wave where it may have been carried by its fluctuations, then our information about the velocity will have real significance. Unfortunately, such a wave is bound to be very extended, so that we cannot keep track of the position of a corpuscle which is wandering about at random. In the opposite case of a wave which is concentrated in a very small area, the corpuscle will stay in much the same position over a longer period, but the phase of the wave will vary to a much greater degree; the fluctuations in the positions of the corpuscle will result in constant changes of velocity, and our knowledge of the velocity will lose its significance.

To sum up: a new interpretation of the uncertainty principle within the theory of the double solution, as described here, expresses the uncertainty of our knowledge of an objective phenomenon which is vitally significant – the subquantum medium.

Stability and quantisation

As stated at the beginning of this chapter, to re-interpret wave mechanics means putting forward a new theory. Once the permanent localisation of corpuscles has been re-established, the theory of measurement must be drastically modified. Therefore, we must next turn to the concepts of stationary state and quantum transition.

Remember that the idea of the quantum state was introduced by Bohr in his first theory of the atom. In this way he was able to account for the emission of the spectral lines, by supposing that an electron emitted one photon when it changed abruptly from one quantum state to another with less energy. In these early researches, Bohr considered that the existence of these states was one of the basic concepts of his theory, and although he drew so much from it he made no attempt to explain it. He believed that an electron can spend a certain time (the mean life-time of the excited state) in that particular state before undergoing a spontaneous transition, and also that the actual transition is instantaneous. An electron cannot exist in any intermediate state between one quantum state and another. Anything of the sort would be 'beyond the possibilities of description in space and time'.

This attitiude was later supported by the interpretation of wave mechanics given by the Copenhagen School. In this conception, it cannot even be said that the electron must be in any particular state, or that it must undergo any particular transition. The transition shows up during a measuring operation, and this operation affects the complex system made up of the electron, the photon, the measuring apparatus and the observer. Before measurement, the electron is 'virtually distributed' between its initial state and all its possible final states, each of which has a certain probability. Only at the instant when the observer notes the arrival in his spectrograph of a photon of a certain frequency, can he cause an abrupt reduction in the packet of probabilities and so claim that the corresponding quantum transition has taken place. The process can still be regarded as instantaneous, but strictly speaking it concerns the reduction of the packet of probabilities rather than the atom itself. Therefore, it is even more hopeless to try to describe the transition 'in the framework of space and time'.

But if we assume that the electron is a corpuscular region constantly *localised* in a wave, we clearly cannot credit that a transition from one state to another can take place without the electron passing through an intermediate stage. It is interesting to note that de Broglie considered this problem even before he put forward his idea of singular waves, and when discussing Bohr's orbits he wrote in his thesis: '. . . we still know nothing about the way in which the transition from one stable orbit to another occurs. The disturbed states accompanying such a transfer can be studied only by means of a suitably modified electromagnetism'.

At about that time, some tentative attempts had been made to deduce the principle of quantisation from some more general law, and it was with this object in mind that G. D. Birkhoff drew up his celebrated theorem on 'central motions'. However, ideas of this kind were forgotten because of the difficulty of the problem, the success of the new mechanics, and the general acceptance of Bohr's ideas. It was only much later that de Broglie's researches caused various investigators to go back to the whole question. It may be appropriate here to recall that many physicists (notably practical experimenters) remained convinced that the concept of instantaneous transition was nothing more than theoretical fiction, and only a few years ago Schrödinger wrote: 'The view that a physical process consists of continual jump-like transfers of energy parcels between microsystems cannot, when given serious thought, pass for anything but a sometimes convenient metaphor'.

We may still be a long way from drawing up a theory capable of describing just how a photon can be emitted during a quantum transition (that is, the formation of a singularity in an electromagnetic field). Still, we can at least investigate another problem which seems more accessible.

Once it has been accepted that an electron passes through a

continuous series of *transient states* between its initial and final quantum states, it must also be accepted that the electron can also be found in a *non-quantised* state, an idea that Bohr rejected. If so, then quantised states are themselves only a few particular states among an infinite number of other possible states, and we must try to understand why they are the only ones to be shown up experimentally (at least up to the present time). In the language of wave mechanics, the question is why the stationary waves are the only states of vibration of the wave of matter to have been recorded, disregarding the particular case of the 'free' movement of the electron.

If we simply say that the stationary states are much more *stable* than any other, it follows that they will last for much longer, and will have a far greater probability of being observed. They will not be the only possible states of the atom, as Bohr thought, but only those which occur for most of the time, and we still have to find out the physical mechanism responsible for such a state of affairs. The main difficulty here is that we have no reason at all for believing, *a priori*, that the transient states satisfy Schrödinger's equation; they may well obey a very different law, which simply happens to take the form of Schrödinger's equation in these special circumstances. However, this result is certainly not inaccessible, because we know of other phenomena which are analogous to those within the atom, and which have been explained by the theory of oscillations. A simple example will show what is meant, even though it does not pretend to provide a model for quantisation.

Consider the pendulum of a grandfather clock. Generally speaking, it appears to have only two possible states of vibration; either it swings to and fro with regular frequency and amplitude, or else it stays motionless in a position of equilibrium, which may be regarded as an oscillation of zero frequency and amplitude. If the pendulum is given a soft tap, it will soon return to its original state, either by losing any extra energy given to it by the tap or by recovering any energy that the tap had taken away. In fact, it behaves as if it soon 'forgets' the perturbation, and we can say that the two states of vibration are *stable*.

If, however, we give a much harder tap, the pendulum can be transferred from one of its states of vibration to the other; we can set it in motion if it was originally at rest, or we can stop it if it was already swinging. The pendulum will reach its new state only after a few more or less disorderly *transient* movements. But since it will stabilise only in one or other of its permanent states, we may conclude that it can gain or lose only an amount of energy which is equal to the energy-difference between the two stationary states. If we could not observe the transient movements, the pendulum would seem to be *quantised*, and the perturbation would cause a jump from one stable state to the other.

It is clear that the analogy between the behaviour of the pendulum and that of the atom is fairly close. If an atom is disturbed by a photon, it may return to its initial quantum state by emitting an identical photon and so getting rid of its excess energy – a phenomenon known as Rayleigh scattering. If the photon is of the appropriate frequency, the atom may however simply absorb it and become raised to a higher quantum energy-state, in which case we have straightforward absorption of light. But if the energy of the photon is great enough, the atom can use part of it to reach a new stationary state and reject the surplus energy in the form of a photon which is less energetic than the incident one. This is known as Raman scattering.

It would be possible to give other similarities between the behaviour of the pendulum and that of the atom, but there are, of course, many atomic phenomena which have no counterparts in the movement of the pendulum. An atom is certainly not a 'clock movement', and the example is useful only because it gives something of a general, albeit vague, analogy.

It may be as well to say something more about the principle of the clock motion. Left to itself, the movement will decrease because of the friction of the mechanism against the pendulum. To keep the swing going, it is necessary to give small periodical impulses by means of a spring, a weight, an electric battery or some other device. If the amplitude of the swing is to remain constant, these impulses must exactly compensate for the loss of energy due to friction. They must therefore come at exactly the right moment (that is, in phase with the oscillation); to increase the oscillation if the pendulum is slowing down or to reduce the swing if the pendulum is starting to move too quickly. An essential mechanical device is the *governor*, which regulates the amount of the swing at each instant according to the state of vibration of the pendulum, and so keeps the movement in a stationary or unchanging state.

A clock mechanism is only one of a great many physical systems capable of controlling their amplitudes and frequencies of oscillation so as to maintain one or more stable modes of vibration. Such systems are called *self-oscillatory*, and the branch of mechanics dealing with them is called non-linear mechanics because of the form of the equations used. The theory was drawn up during the last century following the work of Maxwell and Vichnegradsky on the control of steam-engines, and its mathematical expression is Poincaré's theory of limit cycles. But not until our own century, with the development of radio, electronics and automatic control, was it really systematised. These new branches of science led to the creation of a general theory of control and transmissions, developed twenty years ago by Norbert Wiener under the name of cybernetics, and which is closely linked with the theory of information.

Cybernetics has the additional merit of drawing attention to all the mechanisms which, like the clock escapement, tend to modify an action affecting a physical system as a function of its own state. They are called *feedback mechanisms*, and the theory of information demonstrates their extreme generality and their importance in the laws of nature.

Without attempting a strict analysis, it will be helpful to look at the role of feedback in a clock movement. Imagine a mechanism without feedback (in other words, without a governor) which is meant to keep the pendulum swinging by giving it periodical impulses. It is very clear that there will be many reasons why it will not work. For instance, the impulses disregard the state of motion, so that they cannot compensate for any gains or losses of energy caused by perturbations, and the amplitude of the oscillation will be really out of our control at once. The main difficulty, however, is that there will be no means of keeping the rhythm of the impulses *in phase* with the oscillation of the pendulum, so that even if the pendulum itself were ideally constructed (an unrealistic assumption, of course), the phase would change constantly because of perturbations. It follows that before long the phase of the impulse would be in opposition to the swing of the pendulum; the amplitude of the oscillation would increase and decrease randomly.

A pendulum of this sort could not operate satisfactorily. The motion of the pendulum would depend mainly on the perturbations, and we would be unable to predict its state for any given instant, so that all we could do would be to estimate the probability of its being in one of a great many possible states. Broadly speaking, the movement of the pendulum would be highly 'disorderly'.

Now let us come back to the governor. When the pendulum is freed in any manner whatsoever, it will always return to one or other of its stationary states – the normal swing or else the rest position. The number of possible states has been reduced; disorder has given way to orderliness. But in view of the kinetic theory of matter and the statistical interpretation of entropy as a measure of molecular disorder, we must ask whether it is possible to associate the states of pendulum movement with something resembling entropy, measuring its disorderliness and being reduced by the feedback. This is, in fact, the approach adopted by cybernetics and information theory.

Like any feedback mechanism, the clock governor does no more than send a signal to the source of excitation of the motion; the state of the system can then be controlled so that the required motion can be maintained. For the special cases of auto-oscillatory systems, this required motion is of course a stationary vibration. A certain amount of *negentropy*, or negative entropy, is therefore associated with the transmission of the signal, because the signal reduces the number of possible states of the system; it reduces the disorder, or, in other words, reduces the entropy.

Our generalisation of the feedback and auto-oscillation concepts shows that the method can apply to a vast number of phenomena. This number is even greater than was suggested by non-linear mechanics, because there are many ways of transmitting information: mechanical agencies, electrical or acoustical signals, hormones or other chemical agents, light or radio waves, and so on. Feedback and auto-oscillations can therefore be found in a great variety of phenomena, ranging from the vibration of violin strings to heartbeats, the radiations of certain variable stars, the working of a laser, periodical hormone cycles, the production of electromagnetic waves, the outbreaks of geysers, and industrial control mechanisms.

This list could be considerably extended, but for the moment it is enough to say that outside celestial mechanics, we know of no stationary periodical phenomenon which is not auto-oscillatory. In whatever form this auto-oscillation appears, it is always distinguished by a certain number of modes of stable vibration; more or less abrupt transitions between these stable states are caused by outside influences. Some of these transitions are easy to detect, but others are very much the reverse. If the pendulum of a grandfather clock is disturbed, for instance, its transient states will go on for a considerable number of swings, but if an ordinary wristwatch is shaken the transient motion will not be detectable beyond one oscillation. The transient behaviour of a radio-frequency emitter could not be observed without an oscillograph, and for a laser the detection would be more difficult still.

In view of all these periodical systems, which in practice are observed only in certain stationary states and which seem to make discontinuous jumps between these states, we are led to the question of whether the atom itself can be in auto-oscillation. If so, the quantum transitions would take place very rapidly indeed, but nevertheless in a finite time, so that we ought to be able to describe them, and even to work out experiments which would allow us to follow the process, or at least to measure how long it takes. Quantised states would no longer be the basic concepts of the theory, and it would be possible to gain a deeper understanding of the structures of microsystems.

From this starting-point we could construct 'mathematical models', that is, systems of equations which would not necessarily represent any physical phenomena, but which would lead on to the study of the structure of the mathematical methods of such a theory. Equations have actually been worked out which obey the essential conditions that are required inasmuch as they define a set of privileged states of *stable* vibrations, coinciding with the quantum states and having rapid but finite transitions in between them.

Our most difficult problem is to give a firm expression of the feedback mechanism which controls the stability of the stationary states, and therefore to discover the agent which transmits the signals. Several lines of attack are already known. One of these follows from a hypothesis proposed by de Broglie, according to which a quantum transition must be preceded by what may be called a *warning state* of the atom during which it would emit a continuous electromagnetic wave of very low intensity, capable of controlling the transition process.

Let us now consider these problems from a new viewpoint. It will be seen that considerations which appear at first glance to be very different from those given above do, in fact, lead to essentially the same conclusions.

A hidden thermodynamics

When, in 1905, Einstein proposed the new conception of space and time which is the basis of special relativity, he gave the *coup de grâce* to the ether theories of the nineteenth century, which were already in great difficulty. Yet it would be wrong to infer that relativity is completely opposed to theories of the ether, thereby laying down that space around us can have no hidden properties responsible for certain phenomena.

It is in fact perfectly possible to conceive of ethers which are in agreement with relativity, so long as we avoid defining an absolute frame of reference. Even according to Einstein, the relativistic theory of gravitation introduces a new type of ether. Another ether, of a very different kind, is contained in the interpretation of Dirac's equations, and the quantum theory of fields gives important physical properties to a 'vacuum' containing 'virtual particles' and affected by fluctuations.

It would be difficult to reconcile the old Newtonian picture of inert, passive space with a theory of matter based on the field concept. Not surprisingly, then, de Broglie's double-solution theory has to introduce an ether – the subquantum medium – to justify in particular the principle of interference. This medium is regarded as a kind of huge reservoir of energy in chaotic motion, with particles at the quantum level undergoing never-ceasing fluctuations.

To take this subquantum medium into account, de Broglie has recently developed a *thermodynamics of the isolated particle*. The title is paradoxical, because thermodynamics expresses only the statistical properties of complex systems, for instance, the overall behaviour of atoms and molecules. But if a particle which is 'isolated', in the sense of being well away from any other observable particle, interacts with a hidden medium which is in a state of disorderly agitation, the result is a chaos, analogous to Boltzmann's molecular chaos. It becomes quite natural to suppose that *each particle* will always obey a new thermodynamics drawn from the statistical laws of this chaos, and in which parameters such as temperature, heat and entropy acquire a deeper significance.

The essential problem is to understand the meaning of these parameters in wave mechanics, and therefore to associate them with mass, frequency, wavelength, or other quantities which are fundamental at the atomic level. De Broglie's method of establishing this connection was similar in principle to his first studies about the dual nature of waves and corpuscles; in fact, it may be said to be an extension of them. Before going any further, then, we must recapitulate briefly.

The starting-point of wave mechanics was the idea that every particle of mass **m** is the site of a periodical phenomenon of frequency V. To express this quantitatively, de Broglie joined Einstein's formula $\mathbf{E} = \mathbf{mc}^2$ to Planck's equation $\mathbf{E} = \mathbf{h}V$, obtaining:

$$mc^2 = h\nu$$

which gives a general link between quantum theory and relativity.

To satisfy the relativity principle, *this law must be the same for all observers moving in a straight line with respect to each other*. But in the relativistic sense, both the mass and the frequency are variable; in other words, they are quantities which change for different observers. They must therefore be made to vary in the same manner, to preserve the equality; but this creates a grave difficulty.

If the mass has a certain value $\mathbf{m_o}$ for an observer who is at rest relative to the particle, then the mass value will be *greater* for an observer who is moving. On the other hand, if the observer at rest measures the periodical motion inherent in the particle and gives it as ν_o, then this frequency will become *smaller* for a moving observer. This, of course, is the famous 'clock paradox'. It must be concluded that the first law is valid for a particular observer, for example the observer at rest; he can define a *cyclic frequency* for the particle, but the value he gives will be incorrect for any other observer. It is said that such a law is now relativistically covariant.

In one sense, wave mechanics was born from a theorem of de Broglie's, according to which everything happens as though there exists a wave which is propagated much more quickly than the particle, remains stationary at a frequency ν_o relative to the observer at rest, and which all observers will constantly see *in phase* with the internal cyclical movement of the particle. De Broglie showed that the frequency of this wave varies from one observer to another *in exactly the same way as the mass*. Therefore, the quantum relation $\mathbf{mc}^2 = \mathbf{h}\nu$ becomes relativistically covariant if we replace the cyclic frequency, referred to from now on by ν_c, with the wave frequency ν.

Now let us come back to the new thermodynamics. De Broglie

has recently reviewed the older work of Planck, Einstein and von Laue, and has shown that their laws must be to some extent modified by relativity. In particular, if entropy is relativistically covariant, that is, of the same value for every observer, heat and temperature cannot be covariant. To show what is meant, consider an observer who is at rest relative to a physical system. If he transfers to the system a quantity of heat Q_o at a temperature of T_o, another observer, who is in a state of uniform rectilinear motion with respect to the first observer, will measure a quantity of heat Q and a temperature T, which are smaller than Q_o and T_o. Temperature and heat are both transformed in the same way, but *inversely* as to the energy and the mass. This is so in spite of the fact that, for reasons which cannot be given here, heat is itself a form of energy. However, this variation in temperature is found to be identical with the cyclic frequency V_c, which de Broglie regarded as being of great importance.

For some time the significance of this fact was not appreciated, because many other physical parameters (volume, for example) show the same variation, and in most cases it was simply thought to be due to coincidence. However, it took on a new meaning when de Broglie, following up an analogy developed by Clausius and Boltzmann, showed that there is a connection between thermodynamics and mechanical oscillatory systems.

All these researchers understood that if we can interpret heat as a *disorderly* form of energy, the distinction between heat and work becomes mainly a difference in scale between the two kinds of motion – one rapid and chaotic, the other slow and orderly. Yet this distinction is also found in phenomena which have no apparent connection with thermodynamics.

For example, let us take the case of a violin with one string in a state of stationary vibration. Run a finger *very slowly* down the string, so as to shorten its vibrating section. In this gradual movement, the only effect that will be felt on the finger is the *mean effect* of the very *rapid* vibrations of the string; the string itself will remain stationary. Analysis shows that this mean effect shows itself as a force tending to push the finger upward. To overcome this work must be done, and the end result is an increase in the energy of vibration.

Note the analogy between this process and the case of a piston which is being forced slowly into a heat-shielded, gas-filled cylinder. Here we have the *slow* motion of the piston and the *rapid* motion of molecular agitation; all that shows up in the movement of the piston is the *mean effect*. Once more we have an opposing force which can be overcome only by doing work. This leads to an increase in the molecular excitation, that is, an increase in the heat of the gas.

Clearly, there is a parallel between the heat-energy of the gas and the vibrational energy of the violin string. Indeed, the parallel is so close that Clausius and Boltzmann even calculated the value of the 'heat' increase of the violin string due to the sliding finger. They found that it must be equal to the product of the stationary vibration, and a mechanical parameter which they termed *action*, associated with the mean energy of vibration. It was their formula which gave the starting-point for the thermodynamics of the isolated particle.

If the particle is the site of a periodic movement, it can be associated with a cyclic frequency v_c which is already known; we can also attribute an 'action' to the particle, after which the Clausius-Boltzmann formula will give the value for the quantity of heat which the particle exchanges with its surroundings. But Clausius' fundamental formula gives this same quantity of heat as a function of entropy; after all, the formula itself corresponds to the definition of entropy in thermodynamics. There must be a connection between the action **A** and the cyclic frequency ν_c on the one hand, and the entropy **S** and the temperature **T** on the other. De Broglie expressed this by the formulae

$$h\nu_c = kT, \qquad \frac{A}{h} = \frac{S}{k}$$

where **h** is Planck's constant and **k** is a thermodynamic constant known as Boltzmann's constant.

Here again relativity enters into the discussion, because the cyclic frequency and the temperature are changed in the same way from one observer to another. This means that the law given in the first formula will be identical for all observers, and the second formula will give exactly the same results. It follows that this scheme of thermodynamics, controlling the heat-exchange between the particle and the subquantum medium, is the same for every observer. Ether as defined in this way cannot betray any absolute motion, and so it does not contradict the relativity principle.

The formulae given above assume that the phenomena are very slow, and that they can occur only near the states of stable thermodynamic equilibrium of the particle; it is natural to associate these states with the *stationary states of wave mechanics*. We can however extrapolate to a more general case where this equilibrium, and hence the stationary state, is not reached. Then, according to Carnot's principle, the entropy of the system must tend toward a maximum value, so that the particle will evolve *irreversibly* toward a state of stable equilibrium, in other words, to a quantum state. It follows that even if the stationary states are not the only states possible, they will have a far greater probability of occurrence than the others, simply because of their thermodynamical stability. An electron will always fluctuate around one of its quantised states, because of the small perturbations that affect it all the time. If the equilibrium is upset by a greater perturbation, the electron will change to another stationary state by a transient process which can be described in space and time.

Without developing this argument any further, it is worth remembering that de Broglie studied these problems by taking into account the fluctuations of the proper mass of the particle. These fluctuations are, of course, due to the continual exchanges of energy between the particle and the subquantum medium. Since the variation in mass depends on the state of the particle, de Broglie was able to show that in some cases the monochromatic states will be by far the most probable.

We can now see how de Broglie's conclusions link up with the ideas described in the preceding paragraph. The similarity becomes even more striking when we note that the stability of the stationary vibrations of an auto-oscillatory system is governed by a function known as a Liapounov function. This has the remarkable property of tending to a maximum or minimum value for the stable states, which reminds us once more of entropy. All in all, it is very encouraging to find that theories based upon ideas so very different in character lead to very similar pictures of the stationary states and quantic transitions.

Moreover, the thermodynamics of the isolated particles opens up the prospect of an even more important synthesis. An analysis which cannot be described here shows that if the particle is in permanent contact with that source of heat which makes up the subquantum medium, the action which occurs in de Broglie's formulae is connected not with entropy, but with another thermo-dynamical function which has rather similar properties: *free energy*. But contrary to entropy, Carnot's principle requires that this function should become minimal for the stable states, and de

Broglie was able to express this in wave mechanics.

The achievement of a stationary state is therefore related to a *principle of minimal free energy*, and since this is now directly connected with the action, then the action too must be at a minimum. The situation joins Maupertuis, famous principle of *least action*, which lays down that the real motions of a moving object are those which reduce its action to a minimum, and from which single hypothesis alone the laws of mechanics can be deduced. Clearly, there is a synthesis between Carnot's principle and that of Maupertuis.

Optics has a law of similar type: Fermat's principle, which states that light will always follow the 'quickest' way from one point to another. In the limiting case, when quantum laws join up with classical laws, the resulting motion of the particle will be governed by the principle of minimum action, provided that we assume that de Broglie's wave obeys Fermat's principle. Therefore, wave mechanics forms a bridge between the laws of optics and those of classical dynamics. And since the thermodynamics of the isolated particle provides a link between the principle of minimum action and the second law of thermodynamics, we arrive at a vast synthesis consisting of the laws of mechanics, optics and thermodynamics. In a single system, joined together, we find the principles of Maupertuis, Fermat and Carnot.

It would be difficult to try to predict what will emerge from this new interpretation of wave mechanics, but the questions that it asks, and the prospects that it opens up, are of immense significance. Quantum mechanics has had great successes, but it certainly cannot be regarded as a complete structure in its formalism and its principles – just as it would be quite wrong to suggest that classical mechanics ended with Newton, or optics with Fresnel. The union of quanta, corpuscles and fields is an idea so subtle and so profound that we cannot pretend that its mysteries have been solved to the point where future development would be limited to a more refined mathematical formalism based upon principles which are already established.

General works

Bohr, N. 1961. *Physique atomique et connaissance humaine*, Gauthier Villars, Paris. Trans. 1962. *Atomic physics and human knowledge*, Wiley, London and New York.

Born, M. 1923. *La théorie de la relativité d'Einstein et ses bases physiques*, Gauthier Villars, Paris. Trans. 1924. *Einstein's theory of relativity*, Methuen, London/Dutton, New York.

Broglie, L. de, 1937. *La physique nouvelle et les quanta*, Flammarion, Paris. Trans. 1953. *Revolution in physics; a non-mathematical survey of quanta*, Routledge, London/Noonday, New York.

Broglie, L. de, 1956. *Perspectives nouvelles en microphysique*, collection '*science d'aujourd' hui*', Albin Michel. Trans. 1962. *New perspectives in physics*, Basic Books, London and New York.

Einstein, A. and Infeld, L. 1948. *L'évolution des idées en physique*, Flammarion, Paris. Trans. 1938. *The evolution of physics*, Cambridge U.P., Cambridge/Simon and Schuster, New York.

Heisenberg, W. 1964. *La nature dans la physique contemporaine*, collection '*Idées*', Gallimard, Paris. Trans. 1961. *On modern physics*, Blond, London/Potter, New York.

Planck, M. 1963. *L'image du monde dans la physique moderne*, collection '*Mediations*', Gonthier, Genève.

1 Two small dark clouds

Boltzmann, L. 1896–8. *Vorlesungen über Gastheorie*, J. A. Barth, Leipzig. Trans. 1964. *Lectures on gas theory*, Cambridge U.P., Cambridge/California U.P., Berkely.

Drude, P. 1900. *Lehrbuch der Optik*, Hirzel, Leipzig. Trans. 1959. *The theory of optics*, Constable, London/Dover, New York.

Dugas, R. 1950. *Histoire de la mécanique*, Le Griffon, Neuchâtel. Trans. 1957. *A history of mechanics*, Routledge, London.

Dugas, R. 1959. *La théorie physique au sens de Boltzmann*, Le Griffon, Neuchâtel.

Gibbs, J. W. 1902. *Elementary principles in statistical mechanics*, Yale Publications, Conn. (2nd ed. 1960. Dover, London and New York).

Lorentz, H. A. 1909. *The theory of electrons*, Teubner, Leipzig. (2nd ed. 1953. Dover, London and New York.)

Mach, E. 1897. *Die Mechanik und ihrer Entwickelung*, Brockhaus, Leipzig. Trans. 1960. *The science of mechanics; a critical and historical account of its development* (6th ed), Open Court Publishing Co., London and Illinois.

Maxwell, J. C. 1873. 2 vols. (3rd ed). *Treatise on electricity and magnetism*, Oxford. (3rd ed. edited by J. J. Thompson. 1953. Bowes, London / Dover, New York.)

Newton, I. 1687. *Philosophiae naturalis principia mathematica*, Smith, London. Trans. 1962. *Mathematical principles of natural philosophy*, Cambridge U.P., London/California University Press, Berkeley.

Planck, M. 1897. *Vorlesungen über Thermodynamik*, Veit, Leipzig. Trans. 1945. (3rd ed). *Treatise on themodynamics*, Dover, London and New York.

Sommerfeld, A. 1943. 6 vols. *Vorlesungen über theoretische Physik*, Becker und Erler, Leipzig. Trans. 1949–52. *Lectures on theoretical physics*, Academic Press, London and New York.

Whittaker, E. 1951–3. *A history of the theories of aether and electricity*, Nelson, London / Philosophical Library, New York.

2 Quanta take over physics

Bohr, N. 1913. On the constitution of atoms and molecules, *Philosophical Magazine* **26,** 1, 476, 857.

Bohr, N. 1922. *Les spectres et la structure de l'atome* (traduction de trois conférences), Hermann, Paris. Trans. 1922. *The theory of spectra and atomic constitution*, Macmillan, London and New York.

Born, M. 1925. *Vorlesungen über Atommechanik*, Springer, Berlin. Trans. 1960. (2nd ed.) *The mechanics of the atom*, Ungar, New York.

Brillouin, L. 1931. (2nd ed). *L'atome de Bohr*, Presses Universitaires de France, Paris.

Einstein, A. 1905. Über einen die Erzeugung und Verwandlung des Lichtes detreffenden Heuristischen Gesichtspunkts, *Annalen der Physik* **17,** 132.

Millikan, R. 1947. *Electrons, protons, neutrons, mesotrons and cosmic rays*, Cambridge U.P., Cambridge/Chicago U.P., Chicago.

Perin, J. 1913. *Les atomes*, Alcan, Paris/Presses Universitaires de France, Paris.

Planck, M. 1900. Zur Theorie des Genetzes des Energieverteilung im Normal-spectrum, *Verhandlungen der Deutschen Physikalischen Gesellschaft* **2**, 237.

Planck, M. 1906. *Vorlesungen über die Theorie der Wärmestrahlung*, Barth, Leipzig. Trans. 1959. (2nd ed). *The theory of heat radiation*, Constable, London/Dover, New York.

Rutherford, E., Chadwick, J. and Ellis, C. C. 1930. *Radiations from radio-active substances*, Cambridge U.P., Cambridge/Macmillan, New York.

Sommerfeld, A. 1919. (1st ed). *Atombau und Spectrallinien*, Fried. Vieweg, Braunschweig. Trans. (from 5th German ed). 1934. *Atomic structure and spectral lines*, Methuen, London/Dutton, New York.

3 The equations know best

Bogliubov, N. N. and Shirkov, D. V. 1957. *Vvedenie v teoriou kvantovannih polei*, *Editions technicho-littéraires*, Moscow. Trans. 1959. *Introduction to the theory of quantised fields*, Interscience, London and New York.

Bohm, D. 1951. *Quantum theory*, Constable, London/Prentice-Hall, New York.

Born, M. and Jordan, P. 1930. *Elementare Quantenmechanik*, Springer, Berlin.

Broglie, L. de, 1925. Recherches sur la théorie des quanta (thèse), *Annales de Physique* **10** (3), 22, Masson, Paris.

Broglie, L. de, 1932. *La théorie de la quantification dans la nouvelle Mécanique*, Hermann, Paris.

Broglie, L. de, 1940–2. *Une nouvelle théorie de la lumière, la Mécanique ondulatoire du photon*, Hermann, Paris. Trans. 1939. *Matter and light; the new physics*, Allen and Unwin, London/Norton, New York.

Dirac, P. A. M. 1928. The quantum theory of the electron, *Proceeding of the Royal Society*, **A 117**, 610.

Dirac, P. A. M. 1930. *The principles of quantum mechanics*, Oxford U.P.,

London and New York.

Heisenberg, W. 1925. Über quantenmechanische Umdentung kinematischer und mechanischer Beziehungen, *Zeitschrift fur Physik* **33**, 879.

Heitler, W. 1936. *The quantum theory of radiation*, Oxford U.P., London and New York.

Pauli, W. 1933. Die allgemeinen Prinzipien der Wellenmechanik, *Handbuch der Physik*, **24**, Springer, Berlin.

Schrödinger, E. 1928. *Abhadlunger zur Wellenmechanik*, recueil des memoires de 1926, Barth, Leipzig.

4 Never look behind the facts

Bohr, N. 1932. *La théorie atomique et la description des phénomènes* (traduction de quatre articles), Gauthier-Villars, Paris. Trans. 1934. *Atomic theory and the description of nature*, Cambridge U.P., Cambridge / Macmillan, New York.

Bohr, N. 1935. Can the quantum-mechanical description of physical reality be considered complete?, *Physical Review* **48**, 696.

Einstein, A., Podolsky, B. and Rosen, N. 1935. Can the quantum-mechanical description of physical reality be considered complete?, *Physical Review* **47**, 777.

Electrons et Photons. 1928. *Rapports et discussions du Cinquième Conseil de Physique Solvay*, Gauthier-Villars, Paris.

Heisenberg, W. 1930. *Die Physikalishen Prinzipen der Quantentheorie*, S. Hirzel, Leipzig. Trans. 1930. *Physical principles of the quantum theory*, Cambridge U.P., Cambridge/Chicago U.P., Chicago.

London, F. and Bauer, E. 1939. *La théorie de l'observation en mécanique quantique*, Hermann, Paris.

Neumann, J. Von, 1932. *Mathematische Grundlagen der Quantenmechanik*, Springer, Berlin. (German text with German–English glossary, Dover, London and New York.

Renninger, W. 1960. Messungen ohne Storung des Messobjekts, *Zeitschrift fur Physik* **158**, 417.

Schrödinger, E. 1935. Die gegenwartige Situation in der Quantenmechanik,

Die Naturwissenschaften **23**, 807, 823, 844.

5 God is strict, but He is not unkind

Bohm, D. 1952. A suggested interpretation of the quantum theory in terms of 'hidden' variables, *Physical Review* **85**, 166, 180.

Bohm, D., Schiller, R. and Tiomno, J. 1955. A casual interpretation of the Pauli equation, *Suppl. Nuovo Cimente* **1**, 48, 67.

Bohm, D. and Vigier, J. P. 1954. Model of the causal interpretation of the quantum theory in terms of a fluid with irregular fluctuations, *Physical Review* **96**, 208..

Broglie, L. de, 1953. *La physique quantique restera-t-elle indéterministe?*, Gauthier-Villars, Paris.

Broglie, L. de, 1956. *Une tentative d'interprétation causale et non-linéaire de la mécanique ondulatoire: la théorie de la double solution*, Gauthier-Villars, Paris. Trans. 1960. *Non-linear wave mechanics; a casual interpretation*, Van Nostrand, London and Princeton, N.J.

Broglie, L. de, 1957. *La théorie de la mesure en mécanique ondulatoire* (*inter prétation usuelle et interprétation causale*), Gauthier-Villars, Paris.

Broglie, L. de, 1963. *Étude critique des bases de l'interprétation actuelle de la mécanique ondulatoire*, Gauthier-Villars, Paris. Trans. 1964. *The current interpretation of wave mechanics: a critical study*, Elsevier, London and New York.

Broglie, L. de, 1964. *La thermodynamique de la particule isolée* (*ou thermo-dynamique cachée des particules*), Gauthier-Villars, Paris.

Broglie, L. de, 1967. *Ondes électromagnétiques et photons*, Gauthier-Villars, Paris.

Fer, F.. 1957. *Les solutions singulières des équations d'onde et la théorie de la double solution*, Bureau de documentation minière, Paris.

Glasko, V. B., Leruste, PH., Terletsky, S. and Chouchourine, S. 1958. Recherche des solutions à bosse dans une équation de champ non-linéaire (en russe), *Journal Experimentalnoï u Theretitcheskoï Physiki* **35**, 452.

Halbwachs, F. 1960. *Théorie relativiste des fluides à spin*, Gauthier-Villars,

Paris.

Hillion, P. 1957. *Interprétation causale de la limite non-relativiste pour l'atome d'hydrogène de la représenatation hydrodynamique de l'équation de Dirac*, I.H.P. Paris.

Janossy, L. 1952. The physical aspects of the wave-particle problem, *Acta Physica Hungarica* **1**, 423.

Lochak, G. 1965. Sur l'hypothèse des quanta et la théorie générale de la stabilité du mouvement in *Prévisions, calcul et réalité*, Gauthier-Villars, Paris.

Mugur-Schächter, M. 1964. *Étude du caractère complete de la théorie quantique*, Gauthier-Villars, Paris.

Silva, J. Andrade e, 1960. La théorie des systèmes de particules dans l'interprétation causale de la mécanique ondulatoire, *Annales de l'Institut H. Poincaré* **16**, 289.

Silva, J. Andrade e, Fer, F., Leruste, PH. and Lochak, G. 1961. Quantification stationnarité et non-linéarité, *Cahiers de Physique* **15**, 210.

Silva, J. Andrade e, Fer, F., Leruste, PH., and Lochak, G. 1962. Problèmes de stabilité pour des systèmes à un grand nombre de degrés de liberté, *Cahiers de Physique* **16**, 1.

Takabayasi, T. 1957. Relativistic hydrodynamics of the Dirac matter, *Prog. Theor. Phys. Sup.* **4**, 1.

Terletsky, Y. P. 1960. Sur la théorie statistique des champs non-linéaires, *Journal de Physique* **21**, 771.

Thiounn, M. 1965. Solutions singulières des équations de Dirac et théorie de la double solution, *Cahiers de Physique* **19**, 53.

Vigier, J. P. 1956. *Structure des micro-objets dans l'interprétation causale de la théorie des quanta*, Gauthier-Villars, Paris.

Acknowledgments

Acknowledgment is due to the following for the photographs in this book. The number refers to the page on which the photograph appears.

26 courtesy British Museum; 29, 44 (top right), 45 (top) courtesy Royal Institution, Britain; 44 (top left) courtesy Science Museum, London; 44 (bottom left) courtesy Libraire Hachette, Paris; 42–3 photo J. Anderson, Westfield College, London; 44 (bottom right), 45 (bottom) © Ronan Picture Library; 73, 112 © Associated Press Photo; 74 photo Lotte Jacobi; 87 © Bodleian Library; 95 © Royal Danish Ministry for Foreign Affairs, Denmark; 117, 140, 156 photo Keystone; 118 photo Professor Sir G.P. Thomson; 143 CERN; 211 photo Ken Moreman.

The diagrams were drawn by Design Practitioners Limited.

Eye and Brain

R. L. Gregory

This book brings together the experimental discoveries of both physiology and psychology to give a detailed description of how we see the world. It investigates the processes involved in our perception of objects, the nature of perceptual learning, and the question whether the perceptual system, developed throughout the evolution of animal forms, is adequate to the new tasks that man has set himself – such as high speed flight and space travel. An important section of the book is devoted to a study of common illusions. It shows how these can be used to throw light on the perceptual mechanism of the brain and relates them to the artist's problem of portraying three dimensions on a flat surface. The book raises issues which are of interest to students of the arts as well as to psychologists, biologists and philosophers.

Some international comments

'Une mine étonnante de renseignements précis sur tout le vaste sujet si important qu'annonce le titre'   *Nouvelles Littéraires* **(France)**

'Som populärvetenskaplig framställning måste man ge denna bok högsta betyg'   *Biblioteksbladet* **(Sweden)**

'Chiunque abbia occhi per vedere e cervello per leggere non si lasci sfuggire questa bella occasione'   *Espresso* **(Italy)**

'Highly successful . . . an exceptionally broad and appealing introduction to current knowledge'   *Science* **(USA)**

'Een betere introductie van de serie was niet denkbaar'
Utrecht Nieuwsblad **(Holland)**

'Professor Gregory not only manages to convey his own excitement about the problems but also to tell the student exactly what he ought to know and in exactly the right way'   *Times Literary Supplement* **(UK)**

The Quest for Absolute Zero

K. Mendelssohn

According to the laws of physics the absolute zero of temperature can never be reached, but it can, in principle, be approached to an arbitrary degree. Louis Cailletet's liquefaction of oxygen in 1877 started a quest for ever lower temperatures which was pursued in laboratories all over the world. More recently absolute zero has been approached to within a few millimetres of a degree centigrade. The phenomena observed at these very low temperatures have led not only to new concepts in physics but also to the beginning of a new technology. The absorbing story of the quest for absolute zero is told here for the first time by an author who through four decades has himself been in the forefront of low temperature research.

Some international comments

'Unusual and utterly fascinating . . . it is intended for undergraduate students of physics, but should be on the bookshelves of a much larger group of readers'   *American Scientist* **(USA)**

'La historia apasionante de la busca del cero absoluto se cuenta por primera vez en este libro por un autor que durante cuatro décadas ha ocupado un lugar sobresaliente en la investigación de las bajas temperaturas y para quein los acontecimientos relatados han constituido una experiencia personal'   *La Nación* **(Argentina)**

'Voor ieder die geinteresseerd is in fysica, is dit een fascinerend boek'
Arnhemse Courant **(Holland)**

'Det är en synnerligen välskriven bok'   *Biblioteksbladet* **(Sweden)**

'Nell'insieme un libro di divulgazione scientifica indubbiamente positivo'
Sapere **(Italy)**

'A remarkable book, as absorbing as a novel and as instructive as the best text-book . . . a classic'   *Chemical Engineer* **(UK)**

Books published or in preparation

Economics and Social Studies

The World Cities
Peter Hall, *London*

The Economics of Underdeveloped Countries
Jagdish Bhagwati, *M.I.T.*

Development Planning
Jan Tinbergen, *Rotterdam*

Human Communication
J. L. Aranguren, *Madrid*

Education in the Modern World
John Vaizey, *London*

Soviet Economics
Michael Kaser, *Oxford*

Decisive Forces in World Economics
J. L. Sampedro, *Madrid*

Money
Roger Opie, *Oxford*

The Sociology of Africa
Jacques Maquet, *Paris*

Science and Anti-Science
T. R. Gerholm, *Stockholm*

Key Issues in Criminology
Roger Hood, *Durham*

Population and History
E. A. Wrigley, *Cambridge*

Poverty
R. G. Hollister, *Wisconsin*

History

The Old Stone Age
Francois Bordes, *Bordeaux*

The Evolution of Ancient Egypt
Werner Kaiser, *Berlin*

The Emergence of Greek Democracy
W. G. Forrest, *Oxford*

The Roman Empire
J. P. V. D. Balsdon, *Oxford*

Muhammad and the Conquests of Islam
Francesco Gabrieli, *Rome*

The Crusades
Geo Widengren, *Uppsala*

The Civilisation of Charlemagne
Jacques Boussard, *Poitiers*

Italian City Republics
Daniel Waley, *London*

The Ottoman Empire
Halil Inalcik, *Ankara*

Humanism in the Renaissance
S. Dresden, *Leyden*

The Rise of Toleration
Henry Kamen, *Warwick*

The Scientific Revolution 1500–1700
Hugh Kearney, *Sussex*

The Dutch Republic
Charles Wilson, *Cambridge*

The Left in Europe
David Caute, *London*

The Rise of the Working Class
Jürgen Kuczynski, *Berlin*

Chinese Communism
Robert North, *Stanford*

Arab Nationalism
Sylvia Haim, *London*

The Culture of Japan
Mifune Okumura, *Kyoto*

The History of Persia
Jean Aubin, *Paris*

A Short History of China
G. F. Hudson, *Oxford*

Philosophy and Religion

New Religions
Ernst Benz, *Marburg*

Christian Monasticism
David Knowles, *London*

The Modern Papacy
K. O. von Aretin, *Darmstadt*

Witchcraft
Lucy Mair, *London*

Sects
Bryan Wilson, *Oxford*

Language and Literature

The Birth of Western Languages
Philippe Wolff, *Toulouse*

French Literature
Raymond Picard, *Paris*

Russian Writers and Society 1825–1904
Ronald Hingley, *Oxford*

Satire
Matthew Hodgart, *Sussex*

The Romantic Century
Robert Baldick, *Oxford*

The Arts

Architecture since 1945
Bruno Zevi, *Rome*

Twentieth Century Music
H. H. Stuckenschmidt, *Berlin*

Folk Music
A. L. Lloyd, *London*

Art Nouveau
S. Tschudi Madsen, *Oslo*

Academic Painting
Gerald Ackerman, *Stanford*

Palaeolithic Cave Art
P. J. Ucko and A. Rosenfeld, *London*

Primitive Art
Eike Haberland, *Mainz*

Expressionism
John Willett, *London*

Psychology and Human Biology

The Molecules of Life
Gisela Nass, *Munich*

The Variety of Man
J. P. Garlick, *London*

Eye and Brain
R. L. Gregory, *Edinburgh*

The Ear and the Brain
E. C. Carterette, *U.C.L.A.*

The Biology of Work
O. G. Edholm, *London*

Psychoses
H. J. Bochnik, *Hamburg*

Neuropsychopharmacology
A. M. Ernst, *Utrecht*

The Psychology of Fear and Stress
J. A. Gray, *Oxford*

The Tasks of Childhood
Phillipe Muller, *Neuchâtel*

The Heart
Donald Longmore, *London*

The Endocrine System
R. Greene, *London*

Doctor and Patient
P. Lain Entralgo, *Madrid*

Chinese Medicine
P. Huard and M. Wong, *Paris*

Zoology and Botany

Animal Communication
J. M. Cullen, *Oxford*

Mimicry in Plants and Animals
Wolfgang Wickler, *Seewiesen*

Migration
Gustaf Rudebeck, *Stockholm*

Lower Animals
Martin Wells, *Cambridge*

The World of an Insect
Rémy Chauvin, *Strasbourg*

Life in the Sea
Gunnar Thorson, *Helsinore*

Primates
Francois Bourlière, *Paris*

The Conservation of Nature
C. Delamare Deboutteville, *Paris*

Plant Variation and Evolution
S. M. Walters and D. Briggs, *Cambridge*

Plant Cells
R. Buvat, *Paris*

The Age of the Dinosaurs
Björn Kurtén, *Helsinki*

Parasites
J. G. Baer, *Neuchâtel*

Physical Science and Mathematics

Energy
Etienne Fischhoff, *Paris*

Crystals and Minerals
Hugo Strunz, *Berlin*

The Quest for Absolute Zero
K. Mendelssohn, *Oxford*

Particles and Accelerators
Robert Gouiran, *C.E.R.N., Geneva*

What is Light?
A. C. S. van Heel and C. H. F. Velzel, *Eindhoven*

Mathematics Observed
Hans Freudenthal, *Utrecht*

Waves and Corpuscles
J. Andrade e Silva and G. Lochak, *Paris* Introduction by Louis de Broglie

Science and Statistics
S. Sagoroff, *Vienna*

Earth Sciences and Astronomy

The Structure of the Universe
E. L. Schatzman, *Paris*

Climate and Weather
H. Flohn, *Bonn*

Anatomy of the Earth
André Cailleux, *Paris*

Sun, Earth and Radio
J. A. Ratcliffe, *Cambridge*

Applied Science

Words and Waves
A. H. W. Beck, *Cambridge*

The Science of Decision-making
A. Kaufmann, *Paris*

Bionics
Lucien Gérardin, *Paris*

Metals and Civilisation
R. W. Cahn, *Sussex*

Bioengineering
H. S. Wolff, *London*

Data Study
J. L. Jolley, *London*

Food and Nutrition
Magnus Pyke